"A GLIMMER OF LIGHT"

An Overview of Great Hunger Commemorative Events in Ireland and Throughout the World

Compiled by

Edited by Don Mullan

Cover Design: Robert Ballagh

Published in 1995 by
CONCERN Worldwide
Camden Street
Dublin 2

ACKNOWLEDGMENTS

The editor gratefully acknowledges the assistance of Mr Tom Maher and Sr Gabrielle McManus, The Famine Commemoration Committee, Tullamore; the Office of the President; the Office of the Taoiseach; Cormac Ó Gráda; CONCERN Development Department and all who have generously contributed information, support and advice in the course of creating this book. Thanks are also due to the generous benefactor who sponsored this publication and who has asked to remain anonymous. Finally, thanks are due to Brother John G. Driscoll, Iona College, New York, whose personal support and friendship have been invaluable.

DEDICATED TO

THE MEMORY OF

Ellen Keane

and

to all
the children of the Earth
who die from
the scandal of hunger
in a world of plenty

and

to all who have given their lives in the service of humanity
and the building of a more just and caring world.

Ellen Keane was aged four years and three months when she died on Grosse Ile, Canada, on May 17th, 1847. She had arrived on the coffin-ship "Syria" which left Liverpool on March 24, carrying 241 passengers. Six days after Ellen's death, a total of 202 passengers from the "Syria" were reported ill.

CONTENTS

ℰ

*The Lazaretto, Grosse Ile, where Ellen Keane died on May 17th, 1847,
aged four years and three months.*

Photo: Michael Quigley

ℰ

PREFACE

$\blacklozenge$

I have just returned from a visit to Rwanda, Burundi and the refugee camps of Zaire and Tanzania, where CONCERN volunteers are working with over 400,000 Rwandan refugees. Since April of last year the carnage and pain has been incalculable. As always, it is the innocent and the children who suffer most.

*W*ith the 150th anniversary of Ireland's Great Hunger, we have the opportunity, as a global community, to do something very special and significant. CONCERN Worldwide is committed to contributing to this unique historical moment and, in the best tradition of all that is good in Irish people, to create, on their behalf, a life-giving memorial to our Famine dead.

*C*ONCERN has over 200 Irish and international volunteers (many with Irish roots) working at this moment with the poorest of the poor throughout the world. Poor people with their own human dignity, culture and social identity, but who, like our own people of 150 years ago, have been dispossessed of their God given right to a fair share of our earth's resources.

*S*ince 1968, CONCERN has grown in strength through the overwhelming generosity of the people of Ireland. The generosity of the Irish people becomes more sharply focused and concentrated at moments of great human tragedy such as we witnessed recently in Ethiopia, Somalia and Rwanda. I have no doubt that this deeply felt concern is triggered by the memory of our own famine experiences over the centuries, especially the Great Hunger of 1845-49.

*D*emands are ever increasing on our work and we have, therefore, decided to reach out to the great Irish Diaspora in the hope that they too, will reflect the generosity of the Irish at home by supporting the work of CONCERN. This important anniversary provides us with the opportunity to reach across the centuries and, in the name of our own Famine dead, try to heal the hurts of history and the on-going wounds of today.

I hope that this publication will be useful in linking all those of Irish origin who are planning to contribute to this important anniversary.

I hope too that CONCERN will continue to be, in the words of our Canadian-Irish volunteer, Wendy Murphy, 'a glimmer of light' to the world's poor. With your help and support we shall.

Aengus Finucane CSSp
Chief Executive
CONCERN Worldwide
Dublin
3 January, 1995

INTRODUCTION

$\blacklozenge$

August 20, 1995, will be an important date in the calendar of the Irish worldwide. This date can be described as the beginning of the 150th anniversary of the so-called Great Famine of 1845 – 49. On that date in 1845, Dr. David Moore first observed the potato blight at Dublin's Botanical Gardens. A week later, a total failure of the potato crop was reported from County Fermanagh and, on September 13, 1845, Dr. John Lindley reported with foreboding the arrival of the potato blight in Ireland:

> "We stop the press with very great regret to announce that
> the potato Murrain has unequivocally declared itself in
> Ireland. The crops about Dublin are suddenly perishing."
> (Gardeners' Chronicle and Horticultural Gazette, London)

Dr. Lindley could not have foreseen the cataclysmic consequences of this discovery on the people, social fabric and culture of Ireland, but his knowledge and instincts warned him that a veil of darkness was descending rapidly. "..... Where will Ireland be in the event of a universal potato rot?" he asked his readership.

Within five years, the answer to Lindley's question was becoming all too clear. The face of Ireland had been changed utterly, its culture deeply wounded, its people horrifically scarred and decimated. Within 30 years, Ireland's population had been almost halved through starvation and the worldwide Diaspora of its people, which continued to haemorrhage for decades after the Great Hunger, had officially ended.

$\blacklozenge$

It doesn't surprise me, therefore, that the Great Famine was a period in our history which academics substantially neglected and which the generations in between were hesitant to discuss. Perhaps, 150 years later, we are only now ready to begin to assess the impact of the Famine on our collective psyche and the immeasurable psychological trauma which it and a long suffering colonial experience visited upon us. Pain and suffering are never easy to confront, and often it is easier to walk away and try to forget.

Neither does it surprise me that, as the 150th anniversary of the Great Hunger begins to dawn, an extraordinary awakening within the Irish worldwide is beginning to take place. It would appear that the Irish community, at home and abroad, is recognising this anniversary as a unique historical moment. A moment when we will, at long last, remember with dignity our Famine dead and begin the process of healing the hurts of our history.

———————◆———————

This book has been compiled by CONCERN Worldwide as a contribution to the commemorative activities currently being planned throughout the world to mark the 150th anniversary of Ireland's Great Hunger.

There was a need for an overview of planned events in Ireland and throughout the world and this is what this publication has attempted to give. It does not claim to be definitive or exhaustive. If there are omissions they were not intentional and we apologise for any hurt such omissions may cause.

It became clear to us that many individuals, societies, official bodies and organisations (including our own), are still in the process of developing their programme of activities. We have chosen, therefore, to provide a general introduction to their plans and some of their activities to date. Perhaps, more importantly, we provide names, addresses, telephone and facsimile numbers, in order to facilitate greater communication and co-ordination between interested groups and individuals. Not surprisingly, we discovered extraordinary creativity and thoughtfulness being brought to bear on this important anniversary.

———————◆———————

We have also decided to include reflective pieces aimed at helping to deepen the commitment of the Irish worldwide to an appropriate and challenging commemoration of the Great Hunger. The first is the full text of President Robinson's tri-lingual address on Grosse Ile on August 21, 1994. This is a powerful and insightful reflection which deserves to be studied and discussed. It helps, we believe, to set the tone and the atmosphere for a truly global commemoration which at once expands our humanity and helps heal the deep wounds of history.

The second is a reflection written by one of CONCERN's most experienced volunteers, Canadian-Irish nurse, Wendy Murphy. On August 19-20, 1994, Wendy participated in a 30 mile pilgrimage from Quebec city to St. Bartier, before crossing to Grosse Ile the following day for President Mary Robinson's historic visit. Wendy's reflection has provided us with the title for this booklet, "A Glimmer of Light".

-------------◆-------------

The epilogue to this publication is the text of Beirut hostage Brian Keenan's reflection on the Great Famine, delivered at Mullagh, Co. Cavan, in 1991. Speaking one year after his release from captivity, Keenan made the challenging statement, *"Famine is a Lie!"*

Don Mullan
Co-ordinator
Great Hunger Project
CONCERN Worldwide
3 January, 1995

ℰ

"Waiting to board ship at Cobh"

From: Illustrated London News, 10th May 1851

Courtesy: National Library of Ireland

ℰ

Address

by

The President of Ireland

Mary Robinson

Grosse Ile

21 August, 1994

℘

"*The potato failure was a natural disaster which affected other countries in Europe at the time. But in Ireland it took place in a political, economic and social framework that was oppressive and unjust. The results were devastating ......*"

President Mary Robinson, Grosse Ile, Canada

℘

---◆---

Islands possess their own particular beauty and Grosse Ile is no exception. But Grosse Ile — Oileán na nGael — L'Ile des Irlandais — is special. I believe that even those coming to this beautiful island, knowing nothing of the tragedy which occurred here, would sense its difference. I am certain that no one knowing the story could remain unaffected.

This is a hallowed place.

We are here not to honour an island, however beautiful, but to recall a human tragedy of appaling dimensions. The relics of this tragedy are all too visible. The mass graves marked with the small white crosses assume an added poignancy in their obvious anonymity. And yet we know that each one represents not just the untimely death but the collapse of dreams, not of one person but of many.

It is proper to reflect on what inspired or drove those ordinary men and women, most of them of limited means, many of them on the brink of destruction, to leave their homeland and set out, many with young children, on a hazardous journey. For too many the alternative to death by starvation was a choice between the workhouse, where families would be split up, or a landlord-sponsored passage to the New World. In either case the cabin would be unroofed and the tenancy surrendered. It was a poor choice.

There is no single reason to explain the disaster of the Great Hunger and the Diaspora to which it contributed greatly. The potato failure was a natural disaster which affected other countries in Europe at the time. But in Ireland it took place in a political, economic and social framework that was oppressive and unjust. The results were devastating in Ireland itself but, abroad, they resulted in the creation or strengthening of Irish communities in many countries including in Canada.

---◆---

Tá dínit le haireachtáil san áit seo más dínit an bhróin féin í. Is ceart agus is cóir dúinn comóradh a dhéanamh ar ár muintir atá faoin bhfód anseo. Ní miste a mheabhrú dúinn féin na coinníollacha uafásach a leag a ngaolta agus a gcáirde ar lár anseo. Sháraigh siad gach constaic. Chuaigh siad i ngleic leis an saol, d'fhás siad agus d'fhorbair siad. Tá sliocht a sleachta faoi bhláth i gCeanada. Is de dhlúth is d'inneach an chomhluadair i gCeanada an mhuintir de bhunadh na hÉireann. D'fhag siad rian nach beag ar gach gné don saol. Nuair a thugann muid chun chuimhne míbhuntáistí na linne, faigheann muid léargas ceart ar a n-éacht. Go fírinneach tá údar againn leis an mórtas o chíne a airíonn muid.

On se rend compte de la vérité de l'inscription en français sur la croix celtique: "Ceux qui sèment dans les larmes moissonneront dans la joie."

Il est juste de réfléchir sur le passé, aussi amer qu'il soit. Il est juste de pleurer la tragédie humaine qui a eu lieu ici. Mais cela ne peut suffire. Il faut également en tirer des leçons. Il y a les faits pénibles de l'époque, les expulsions, la misère, les maladies, les carences de la justice, la négligence, et jusqu'à la responsabilité des pouvoirs politiques, qui illustrent le côté noir de la vie, mais il y a aussi de quoi nourrir notre espoir.

Parce qu'en dépit des difficultés et du danger réel qui mettaient leur vie en jeu, l'action des Canadiens et des Canadiennes a été magnifique. Ailleurs, sur le continent, on fermait les portes à l'arrivée des Irlandais. Au Canada, le peuple — et en particulier le peuple de Québec — a fait preuve d'une compassion tout à fait extraordinaire à l'égard des Irlandais, hommes et femmes, indigents et malades.

Le clergé, tout autant protestant que catholique, a apporté soulagement aux malades et soin aux survivants. Parmi ces prêtres se trouvait Elzéar Alexandre Tascherau, qui devait devenir le premier Cardinal-Archevêque du Canada.

A Montréal ce sont les Soeurs Grises qui ont soigné les malades dans les "hospital sheds" (abris de secours) spécialement construits pour les immigrés Irlandais. Et quand à leur tour elles sont tombées malades, ce sont les Soeurs de la Charité qui les ont remplacées. Il faut également se souvenir du Maire de Montréal, Mr. John Mill, qui lui-même a trouvé la mort en soignant les malades.

To all of those brave and compassionate people, lay and religious, Anglophone and Francophone, Catholic and Protestant, in Quebec and elsewhere in Canada, who at great personal risk, aided and cared for the sick and destitute Irish and gave homes to Irish orphans, we owe a debt of gratitude. I pay tribute to their memory on my own behalf and on behalf of the people of Ireland. In the words of Máirtín Ó Direáin, a poet from another beautiful island:

"Maireann a gcuimhne fós i m'aigne
Is mairfidh cinnte go dté mé i dtalamh."

--------------- ◆ ---------------

In this place of memory and regret I think we have a chance to reflect on our relation to the past. The men and women who came here in the 1840s and died, were helpless before a historical catastrophe of enormous proportions. It is their very helplessness which can mislead us into believing that we also are helpless in our attitude to a past we cannot control and can never change. But we are not. We have the chance to choose today between being spectators or participants at the vast theatre of human suffering which unfolds throughout human history.

If we are spectators then we will choose the view that there are inevitable historical victims and inevitable survivors. And from that view, I believe, comes a distancing which is unacceptable and unmoral.

If we are participants, then we realise there are no inevitable victims. We refuse the temptation to distance ourselves from the suffering around us — whether it comes through history books or contemporary television images. And then, although we cannot turn the clock back and change the deaths that happened here, at least we do justice to the reality of the people who died here by taking the meaning of their suffering and connecting it to the present day challenges to our compassion and involvement. If we are participants we engage with the past in terms of the present. If we are spectators then we close these people into a prison of statistics and memories, from which they can never escape to challenge our conscience and compassion.

--------------- ◆ ---------------

Earlier this year I opened the Famine Museum at Strokestown House in Roscommon. There, also, were images of suffering and desolation. There, also, our sense of horror was tempted towards a sense of fatalism. Ironically, many people from Roscommon took ship for Canada. In each case the story is the same. What is variable is our determination to do honour to those events by an active relation to them. And therefore, as President of Ireland, and in memory of so many who died here, I think I can say that what is particularly Irish about this occasion is not simply the nationality of those who died here. It is also our sense, as a people who suffered and survived, that our history does not entitle us to a merely private catalogue of memories. Instead, it challenges us to consider, not just little Ellen Keane, the four year old child who was the first to die here in 1847, but the reality is that children are usually the first victims of famine and displacement. It challenges us, in her name, to consider with compassion and anger those other children to whom we can give no name who are dying today in Rwanda and whom I saw in the camps in Somalia.

———————◆———————

Next year commemorates the 150th year since the famine which devastated Ireland. No one then could have foreseen, or even hoped, that a modern European state would emerge, with a powerful identity and a confident culture. It is very important to me that within that culture, the voiceless, desolate dead of such places as Grosse Ile, are remembered and honoured. We owe to their humiliation at the hands of fate just as much love and respect as to any brave or decisive action which turned the tide of history in our favour. But it is also important that as a people who have seen the dark and the bright face of such fortunes we take the initiative not just in compassionate action towards those who are now caught, as we once were, in famine and disease, but also in re-defining the contemporary attitude to such suffering.

We are in the presence, even as I speak, of an enormous historic irony. The ease and proliferation of communication has had, I believe, the result of isolating us further from one another. The presence of death in our living rooms, the images of horror invite us to feel helpless and fatalistic. Perhaps the real justice we can do these people here and those who died throughout our famine — perhaps the best way to commemorate them —is to think decisively and creatively about the supply and distribution of such ordinary commodities as food and water.

It may be less glamourous than standing in a posture of grief and regret. But a careful and analytical study of just how little, for instance, has been done to distribute clean water to areas of large slum dwellings or refugee camps is both vital and overdue. And if this seems too ordinary a detail, I think we should remember that the thousands who died here, whose dreams were extinguished, whose future was lost on this island, died, because of the detail of the failure of one crop. There are such details all over the world now, but particularly in Africa, which need our urgent attention.

Grosse Ile is not simply a place to commemorate the past and honour those who are buried here. In essence, it is a resource to connect us with the terrible realities of our current world. It challenges us to reject the concept of inevitable victims and, having done so, to face up to the consequences of that rejection.

———————◆———————

President Mary Robinson pictured during a visit to CONCERN's Head Office in Dublin on the occasion of the organisation's 25th Anniversary.

Photograph: Tom Connolly

Grosse Ile, Canada

A Reflection

by

Wendy Murphy
CONCERN Volunteer

❧

*Quebec City, August 1994. Pilgrims gather before the 30-mile walk
to Grosse Ile. Wendy Murphy stands centre, behind banner.*

Photo: Michael Quigley

❧

---◆---

Fortunately, my ancestors survived the challenge of immigration. So in 1862 my paternal great-grandmother, Ellen Kane, was born in Ontario. She had been given a name very similar to the first person documented to have died on Grosse Ile in 1847, Ellen Keane. Ellen Keane was just four years old when she died. But my great-grandmother lived until she was 78, leaving more relations than I know. The lives of both Ellens have, unknowingly, influenced my own.

My linkage with Grosse Ile continues with my maternal ancestors. They passed by the island in 1898-99. Remaining true to their belief of pacifism within their Doukhabour faith, they were fleeing persecution in Russia. They had been guaranteed freedom and farming opportunities in Canada.

So when the invitation for me to join a pilgrimage to Grosse Ile arose last August, rather suddenly, my response was just as quick. When the decision was made, it was without the realisation of how much history would be discovered there; our history of 150 years and my own history of today.

Volunteering with VICS (Volunteer International Christian Services), a Canadian organisation, transplanted me a few years ago to live and work among the Gedeo people in rural Ethiopia. Those two brief years were full of many challenges. Consequently, they were formative of my faith in the poor.

Subsequent to Ethiopia, time was spent in Southern Sudan and Somalia operating feeding centres for famine victims with CONCERN. As during the Irish Famine, these people are victims not only of crop failure but also of oppression and poverty.

---◆---

The Grosse Ile pilgrimage began on August 19, with 12 of us setting off on a 30 mile Famine walk, over two days from Quebec City to St. Bertier. As we walked, marched and, admittedly, sauntered, we talked. We shared. We healed some of our individual sorrows that life had given us. More walkers joined us en route, for a total of 25 who crossed the threshold at the end point of the St. Bertier church. On the third and final day of the pilgrimage, August 21, the buses from Toronto and Ottawa had arrived. Others had driven from Montreal to boost our numbers to over 450. It was on that Sunday we were ferried over to Grosse Ile to see the island of tragic history. There, we developed a small but lasting sense of what had really occurred.

As Ellen Keane proves, the children are the most vulnerable and they pay in the greatest numbers. A poor nutritional state, contaminated water and confined living conditions are breeding grounds for communicable diseases. Cholera and typhus were rampant aboard the timber ships. Today such diseases continue to kill thousands of people in the 'Developing World'. These are the same diseases for which the quarantine station on Grosse Ile was established. But the facilities and personnel were quickly overwhelmed, leading ultimately to the burial of thousands of dead in mass graves.

---------------- ◆ ----------------

The final day of the pilgrimage was cool and rainy. In eerie silence I looked over the grave site on Grosse Ile which has been cleared from the overgrowth. Exact numbers vary, but around 15,000 are buried there. In my mind, I was back in Afgoi, Somalia, 1993, where mass graves are scattered. Some were buried in designated areas, others wherever they died and where the earth was sufficiently soft. None of the graves are marked. They are just mounds of dirt. Two incidents resurfaced in my mind. The first being a young American soldier, who finally mounted the courage to ask the question they all had:

"Over there, ma'am?" in his American drawl.
"Yes?"
"Just outside the gate of the feeding centre?"
"Yes?"
"Are they graves ma'am?"
"Yes. You are in Somalia, you know," was my reply.

The second incident was back in Mogadishu during our evening meal. The discussion that night centred on what to do with the graves in the court yard of one of the schools CONCERN was refurbishing. Should we mark them and leave them? Fence them off? Move them? Graveyards are sacred places. Holy ground. The decision was to leave them undisturbed and marked.

Overlooking the site of the mass graves on Grosse Ile there is a memorial erected in honour of the medical personnel who had come from Quebec and Ireland to care for the ill. Epidemiological knowledge about cholera and typhus was limited. So the doctors too succumbed to the diseases they had hoped to treat.

That fact and the memorial took me back to Somalia again. This time, in my mind, I was not in the feeding centre. We were driving down the road from Afgoi to Wanle

Wein. Unsuspectingly, we were caught in a hail of bullets. At the end of it all my friend and colleague, Valerie Place, was dead. She had not died from cholera or starvation but from the sickness of war. Organised or random, it is an illness that knows no limits.

At the Pan Africa centre in Mogadishu where Valerie had been working, the local staff have paid tribute. An artist was hired to paint a depiction of Valerie cradling a marasmic and dehydrated child. It is a scene of the compassion that so easily flowed out of her. The mural is fenced off and flowers planted around it. In Ireland, other memorials have been established to honour Valerie's life and death.

———————◆———————

*F*or many, the highlight of the pilgrimage to Grosse Ile was the address given by President Mary Robinson. Indeed in her graceful manner, she delivered a thoughtful and challenging speech, connecting the history of Grosse Ile with the challenges of today's world.

But for myself, the most poignant moment was crossing over to the island. A few of us had been assigned to the first sailing. An early departure from Quebec City was necessary to catch the 6a.m. ferry, a small boat. In the early morning light, the sky was overcast, as grey as the river.

We crossed in silence, each lost in our own thoughts as the boat gently rocked down the St. Lawrence. Unlike the timber ships, there were small windows, emitting the muted daylight. Like those who journeyed here before us, we were anxious for what awaited us on the island. The difference, of course, ours was a one day return trip. As we approached the island it was mysterious and foreboding. They of 1847, and later, fled their homeland filled with a desperate hope for a better life. This dark island of death was their initial welcome.

People have often asked me why, as a Canadian, I have chosen to work with an Irish based organisation. Assuming that most people would not understand if I was to answer "because of Ellen Keane," my usual answer is because of the renowned expertise in responding to a famine crisis, the Irish have acquired. This leads to the next obvious question of why that expertise has come about. The answer is simple. Out of their own darkness they have become a light. Graciously I have been able to share in a glimmer of that light.

———————◆———————

ℒ

"At the Pan Africa Centre in Mogadishu where Valerie had been working ....
an artist was hired to paint a depiction of Valerie cradling a marasmic
and dehydrated child. It is a scene of the compassion
that so easily flowed out of her."

Wendy Murphy

ℒ

Overview

Of

Great Hunger

Commemorative Events

§ 1. IRELAND

1.1 ARTS
1.1.1 Cashel Heritage Society
1.1.2 Donegal Workshop Theatre
1.1.3 Galway Youth Theatre
1.1.4 "Journal"
1.1.5 "The Country Blooms; A Garden and a Grave" Exhibition
1.1.6 The Galloping Cat Theatre Company
1.1.7 Waterford Youth Drama
1.1.8 West Waterford Drama Festival Committee

1.2 DEVELOPMENT/RELIEF AGENCIES
1.2.1 AFrI
1.2.2 CONCERN
1.2.3 Dochas
1.2.4 Trócaire

1.3 HISTORICAL/CULTURAL /SCIENTIFIC ORGANISATIONS AND PROJECTS
1.3.1 Bandon Historical Society
1.3.2 Carrick-on-Shannon and District Historical Society
1.3.3 Comhaltas Ceoltóirí Éireann
1.3.4 European Association for Potato Research
1.3.5 Federation for Ulster Local Studies
1.3.6 Irish Family History Foundation
1.3.7 Irish Organic Society
1.3.8 Isht Ikhana, Community College, Dunshaughlin
1.3.9 Kells Enterprise Group
1.310 Knockfierna Heritage and Folklore Group
1.3.11 National Botanic Gardens
1.3.12 National Graves Association
1.3.13 St. Cronan's Workshop
1.3.14 The "Jeanie Johnston" Project
1.3.15 Tidy Towns Association, Rathkeale, Co. Limerick
1.3.16 Workhouses of the West Project

1.4 IRISH GOVERNMENT & AGENCIES
1.4.1 Office of the Minister of State, Department of the Taoiseach
1.4.2 Department of Agriculture, Food and Forestry/Teagasc
1.4.3 Local Authorities

§   2   **BRITAIN**

§ 3   CANADA

§ 4   U.S.A.

§ 5   # AUSTRALIA/NEW ZEALAND

§ 6   # SOUTH AFRICA

§ 1.   IRELAND

1.1 ARTS

1.1.1 Cashel Arts and Heritage Society
c/o Folk Village
Cashel
Co. Tipperary
Telephone: 062-62525
Fax: 062-62322
Contact Person: Mr Danny O'Dwyer

The Cashel Arts and Heritage Society is currently in the process of producing a play/pageant to commemorate the 150th Anniversary of the Great Famine through drama, music, song and dance. An Ghorta Mhór will run from Mondays to Fridays, from June 19 to September 25 of 1995/96/97. The Society also intends to make a "video/film" on the Famine in the near future. An Ghorta Mhór will be preceded by sequences of Street Theatre in Cashel Town. During the show's interval, the audience will be able to sample Mr. Soyer's infamous famine soup in the Society's authentic soup kitchen.

The aim of the Cashel Arts and Heritage Society is to preserve Ireland's heritage and culture through the Arts and, if successful, to help CONCERN's famine relief work in Third World countries.

1.1.2 Donegal Workshop Theatre
Rosbeg
Portnoo Post Office
Co. Donegal
Telephone: 075-45162
Contact Person: Ms Dixi Patterson

The Donegal Workshop Theatre has produced a one and a half hour play entitled "Hungry for Change". It is described as a "Startling new piece of theatre depicting the fate of a small Donegal community living in a cluster of cottages on a landlord's estate in the 1840s."

Eight members of the Teenage Drama Group assisted the play's director and scriptwriter, Dixi Patterson, in doing backstage research over a two year period.

Mairéad, a central character in the play, asks the question "Will it ever change?" "Sadly," says Patterson, "it hasn't changed; echoes still reverberate in 1994. The so-called famine may have moved to other shores, different fingers may pull the triggers, but for many the struggle for survival has become even more desperate."

1.1.3 Galway Youth Theatre
47 Dominick Street
Galway
Telephone: 091-65886/68303
Contact Person: Ms Rebecca Bartlett

The Development Education Department of CONCERN is currently involved with the Galway Youth Theatre in developing a production for the 1995 Galway Arts Festival on the theme of "Famine". The play will be mainly written and produced by Rebecca Bartlett who is being resourced by the CONCERN Development Education Department.

In addition, a script writing competition for mid-west schools was supported by both CONCERN and Galway Youth Theatre. The winning scripts were staged in Galway in early December, 1994, and will have several countrywide performances which began in Kilkenny on January 5th, 1995.

1.1.4 "Journal"
Killucan
Co. Westmeath
Telephone: 044-74781
Contact Person: Ms Geraldine O'Reilly

In 1988 Geraldine O'Reilly produced an exhibition under the collective title "Journal", which documented the emigrants' journey from Cobh to New York. The period she dealt with was the immediate aftermath of the Great Famine until the 1930s. O'Reilly did extensive research into Irish/American labour history of this period, funded by a Fulbright Scholarship. She used numerous pieces of text from academic studies on Irish emigration and also excerpts from emigrant letters and newspapers. The exhibition consisted of 19 images, all done in mixed-media. It opened at the Triskel Arts Centre, Cork and numerous pieces were selected for the Guinness Peat Aviation awards for "Emerging" Artists Exhibition, at the Douglas Hyde Gallery, Trinity College.

O'Reilly had two subsequent exhibitions which dealt with themes of identity and emigration. Most of this work was based on a set of emigrant letters entitled "Curtiss Papers", which is housed in the Balch Institute, Philadelphia, PA.

One piece from the "Journal" exhibition entitled "57 immigrant ships lost, 1847-1857" was used by Lilliput Press for the front cover of "The Great Famine; Studies in Irish History". The title of the painting refers to the number of ships lost in Liverpool harbour, carrying Irish emigrants, even before they began their trans-Atlantic voyage. It is taken from an article which appeared in the Liverpool Gazette (1857).

O'Reilly is currently working on a new exhibition on identity, displacement, homeland and borders, with specific reference to the pain of emigration.

1.1.5 "The Country Blooms; A Garden and a Grave" Exhibition.
70 Eccles Street
Dublin 7
Telephone: 01-8302652
Contact Person: Ms Alanna O'Kelly

Alanna O'Kelly has produced a series of works since 1990 under the general heading "The Country Blooms; A Garden and a Grave", based on and with reference to the Irish Famine during the period 1846–48. Her works, which include photo-text works, multi-monitor video works, single video works, sound works, installations and live performances, have been exhibited extensively throughout Ireland, Europe and North America.

O'Kelly is currently preparing to exhibit part of her Famine Exhibition at the George Pompidou Centre, Paris. Pól Brennan, ex-Clannad member, has worked with O'Kelly on the Paris Exhibition.

The introduction to her exhibit "No Colouring can Deepen the Darkness of Truth", which opened at the Irish Museum of Modern Art, September 1992, is quoted here in full:

> For a long time I have known of a need
> to take a look at the great Irish Famine of 1846-1848.
> The interest has been to do with this incredible event
> as a time of absolute change for us on this island.
> The changes wrought on our language, our culture, our psyche,
> continue to impact on us as contemporary realities.
> The issues of the Great Famine are alive

monumental and devastating, here are areas
of immense sadness, anger, humiliation,
confusion, dignity and healing.

Our families' stories, memories,
unspoken pain, fear and hurt lie everywhere.
Patterns of history repeating themselves —
Our story, yet, hardly talked about
displaced, unsettled, denied and dispossessed.
A scattered people
we share with others this despised experience.
Similar conditions continue to write new Histories today.
A common story we can begin to recognise.
A common ground to heal.

1.1.6 Galloping Cat Theatre Company
c/o City Arts Centre
23-25 Moss Street
Dublin 2
Telephone: 01-6770643
Contact Person: Mr Gerry Morgan

Produced in 1991, "Farewell to Kind Relations", based on a coffin-ship crossing to America, is an excellent production with immense potential for the forthcoming 150th anniversary.

"Farewell to Kind Relations" is a compelling account of an escape: an escape from fear and hunger, a journey from despair to hope. It follows a voyage from Ireland to America during the Great Famine, an almost forgotten time in our past, here vividly recalled.

Performed in the round on an open stage, "Farewell to Kind Relations" takes the audience at first hand on board a Famine ship, reliving the experiences of ordinary Irish people on a desperate quest for life and dignity. At times harrowing and tragic, at times infused with inspiring humour, the play is a tribute to the courage and tenacity with which our ancestors clung to life and hope.

"Devastating Theatre, exciting, moving and even funny. Demands to be seen."
(Irish Times)

Galloping Cat Theatre Company is a professional company dedicated to celebrating in theatrical form the popular Irish traditions of storytelling and music. This play has been devised by the company from original research documents.

In association with AFrI and CONCERN, this play will be made available to schools and the general public throughout the period 1995-97.

1.1.7 Waterford Youth Drama
15 Broad Street
Waterford
Telephone: 051-79377
Fax: 051-55109
Contact Person: Mr Ollie Breslin

Waterford Youth Drama will present "The Stick Doll" by Ted O'Regan, at the Garter Lane Theatre, Waterford, from Wednesday 26th - Saturday 29th April, 1995.

"The Stick Doll" is a play for and researched partly by children aged between 10 and 14 years. It explores the plight of the common people, the indifference of some landlords, the charity of groups like the Quakers, the hardship of the workhouses, and the — for some — happy endings.

1.1.8 West Waterford Drama Festival Committee
Glenbeg
Glencairn
Co. Waterford
Telephone: 058-54128/60367
Fax: 058-54877
Contact Person: Mr Richie Walsh

"Ocras", an Irish word for "Hunger", is the title of a project currently being developed by the West Waterford Drama Festival Committee. The project intends to examine the famine at a local level in West Waterford and North-East Cork and place it in its national context. Over a three year period a variety of events are planned including lectures, theatrical re-enactments, pageants, video presentations, exhibitions, historical research, school competitions and the collection of any relevant folklore. The programme of events for 1995 will be announced in the springtime of 1995.

The Drama Committee's promotional brochure states: "...statistics are terrifyingly stark and yet, the Great Famine as a social catastrophe has been somewhat neglected by historians and researchers both local and national. It is as if it left such a deep psychological scar that we as a nation have preferred to almost forget it actually happened than to rake through extremely painful and relatively recent memories...

"...One hundred and fifty years on, we now look back without sentimentality or anger to see what really happened, being ever-mindful of the fact that the scourge of famine continues to plague the world at large and we ask, for ourselves and for others, for the past and for the present...Why?

The project is dedicated to "the millions forced to emigrate during and after the famine...but also to those who stuck it out...to the people of Ballyduff and Ballysaggart... The Survivors".

1.2 DEVELOPMENT/RELIEF AGENCIES

1.2.1 AFrl
The Cottage
63 Harold's Cross Road
Dublin 6W
Telephone: 01-4966880
Fax: 01-4966388
Contact Person: Mr Joe Murray

In 1984, AFrl's Great 'Famine' Project was inspired by Archbishop Desmond Tutu of South Africa during a short visit to Ireland. AFrl was the first organisation in the Irish world to recognise the importance of the approaching 150th anniversary which it describes as "a unique historical moment". The two leading "Third World" agencies in Ireland, CONCERN and Trócaire, are now working closely with AFrl in ensuring that AFrl's aim of drawing the links and parallels between Ireland's Great Hunger and world hunger today are achieved.

The aims of AFrl's Great 'Famine' Project are:

* *To ensure that the 150th anniversary of Ireland's Great 'Famine' is commemorated in a dignified and challenging way, both nationally and internationally.*
* *To publicly honour Ireland's several hundred unmarked mass 'Famine' graves with dignity and reverence.*
* *To harness the memory of Ireland's Great 'Famine' experience as a window through which the Irish (at home and abroad) can better understand the cause and effect of poverty and hunger on the world's poor today — and to encourage an appropriate response.*

In 1990, AFrl brought to national and international attention the story of the

Choctaw Indians' generosity towards Irish Famine Relief in 1847. In 1992, AFrI had a plaque unveiled to the Choctaw by the Lord Mayor of Dublin, in the Mansion House, Dublin. On that occasion President Mary Robinson received the Choctaw Delegation at Áras an Uachtaráin during which she was given the title "Honorary Chief of the Choctaw Nation of Oklahoma", the first woman in the history of the Choctaw to be given this honour. Following their participation in the AFrI 'Famine' Walk, the Choctaw began a re-enactment of their own "Trial of Tears" (1831) which is now an established annual event between Arkansas and Oklahoma. Other Walk leaders have included Archbishop Desmond Tutu (1991), who attempted to alert the "Western World" to the unfolding famine in Somalia; Brian Keenan, Beirut hostage (1991), who spoke on the theme "Famine is a Lie"; and Joanne Tall (1992), representing the Oglala Sioux of South Dakota. On this occasion Irish people acknowledged the role of our forebears (many of them 'Famine' emigrants) in the brutal colonisation of the Plains Indians.

In 1991, the Irish American Cultural Institute (IACI) invited AFrI to participate in its Irish Perceptions Lecture Tour in order to outline the importance of the approaching 150th Great 'Famine' commemoration. AFrI did so in Los Angeles; Cincinnati; Chicago; Charlotte, North Carolina; Phoenix, Arizona; New Jersey; Topeka, Kansas; Detroit; Montreal; Pittsburgh, Pennsylvania and St. Paul, Minnesota. The Tour was described by the IACI as: "the most well received in recent years."

In addition, with the support of Br. John G. Driscoll, Iona College, New York, AFrI has visited Connecticut, New York, Boston, Philadelphia and Quebec. Many of the seeds which AFrI spread during these visits are now bearing fruit.

An example of this can be gauged in the programme of events currently being planned by the Wild Geese (see 4.2.5) whom AFrI befriended in the Fall of 1989.

Recognising the importance of Irish Government involvement in the Great 'Famine' commemoration, AFrI met with Mr. Tom Kitt, T.D., former Minister of State at the Department of the Taoiseach and Foreign Affairs, on October 13, 1993. AFrI presented a paper to the Irish Government emphasising the importance of the approaching anniversary and suggesting five possible contributions the Government might consider. These included linking an increase in Ireland's ODA to the anniversary years of 1995-2000; a commemorative stamp in association with the postal services of the US, Canada, Britain, New Zealand, Australia and Argentina; the erection of a national monument in the West of Ireland; support for AFrI's determination that the hundreds of forgotten mass Famine graves be set aside with simple dignity, with a commitment to have them cared for after the anniversary years; support for a symbolic Atlantic crossing in 1997, with a mid-ocean service, remembering the hundreds of thousands of Irish refugees who died at sea whilst fleeing the 'Famine'. AFrI emphasised that causes of contemporary "famines" should be central to whatever the Government does — causes such as debt, the arms trade, the inequitable distribution of wealth and resources.

Mr. Kitt attended AFrI's seventh annual 'Famine' Walk at Louisburgh, Co. Mayo, on 4 May 1994. He informed the gathering that the then Taoiseach, Mr Reynolds, had instructed him to set up an inter-departmental committee at the Department of the Taoiseach. The committee has the specific brief of examining ways through which the Irish Government might make a significant contribution to the 150th anniversary of the Great 'Famine'. Mr. Kitt also stated he expected AFrI to play a leading role in these events. Since then the Minister has invited an input into the Government committee from individuals and groups interested in contributing to the 'Famine' commemoration (see 1.4.1).

Since 1989, AFrI has been working with Paddy Moloney of the Chieftains on the creation of a Great 'Famine' Symphony. Supported by CONCERN, this symphony is due to have its world premier in Quebec City in July 1995.

AFrI has already begun the process of marking 'Famine' burial sites throughout Ireland. It is currently working with schools and local groups in identifying burial places and preparing to have them marked.

At the request of St. Patrick's Society of Montreal, AFrI was invited to present a brief at a Public Hearing conducted by Parks Canada in Montreal on May 20, 1992, concerning their "Development Concept" for Grosse Ile. On 5 March 1993, AFrI wrote to President Robinson asking her to consider a visit to Grosse Ile on any future visit to Canada. Her secretary replied saying she would. On 21 August 1994, at the beginning of her first official visit to Canada, the Irish President made an historic visit to Grosse Ile.

As part of its on-going project, AFrI plans two 'Famine' walks during 1995; to continue its research project aimed at locating mass 'Famine' graves and their marking; a 10k run in association with CONCERN; to help develop the Development Education aspects of the Louisburgh Great Famine Centre; mount a photographic exhibition in association with photographer Derek Spiers and to host a performance of a 'Famine' play. AFrI has been greatly encouraged by the number of groups, individuals, organisations and official bodies, including the office of the President, who have maintained contact with the agency and are now echoing their main aim which is to ensure the world's poor are not forgotten during this unique historical moment.

1.2.2   **CONCERN** Worldwide
Camden Street
Dublin 2
Telephone: 01-4754162
Fax: 01-4757362
Contact Person: Mr Don Mullan

The Development Education Department of CONCERN is currently involved with the Galway Youth Theatre in developing a production for the 1995 Galway Arts Festival on the theme of "Famine". The play will be mainly written and produced by Rebecca Bartlett who is being resourced by the CONCERN Development Education Department.

In addition, a script writing competition for mid-west schools was supported by both CONCERN and Galway Youth Theatre. The winning scripts were staged in Galway in early December, 1994, and will have several countrywide performances which began in Kilkenny on January 5th, 1995.

CONCERN is currently developing a wide-ranging commemorative programme for the 150th anniversary of the Great Hunger. Events will include a 10k run, Paddy Moloney's Famine Symphony, an Irish pilgrimage to Grosse Ile and many other initiatives involving its Dublin, Belfast, London, Glasgow and New York offices. CONCERN commemorative events will also include its many volunteers working in emergency relief and long term development projects in over 15 countries worldwide.

Given CONCERN's extensive experience in working with the victims of famine in areas such as Biafra, Bangladesh, Ethiopia, Sudan, Somalia and Rwanda, the agency believes it has an important perspective, grounded in the reality of contemporary human suffering, to bring to current commemorative events.

Recognising the important role which the agency AFrI has played in ensuring the world's poor are on the agenda of the 150th anniversary of the Great Famine, CONCERN has willingly supported its work.

1.2.3 DOCHAS
59 Deerpark Road
Mount Merrion
Co. Dublin
Telephone/Fax: 01-2886141
Contact Person: Ms Anna Farrell

Dochas is the Irish Association of Non-Government Development Organisations. It plans two initiatives for the coming year. This involves a part-time research worker who will assist in preparing a position paper and conference. The aim of the position paper will be to help Dochas and others concerned with development, reflect on the experience of the Great Famine, to understand more fully and address more effectively, famine and food insecurity in our own times.

The research worker has commenced work and the National Famine Conference is planned for February 1995.

1.2.4 TRÓCAIRE

169 Booterstown Avenue
Blackrock
Co. Dublin
Telephone: 01-2885385
Contact Person: Dr Colm Regan

Trócaire is involved in a three way project involving the Ulster Folk and Transport Museum, and Strokestown Park House. An education pack for secondary schools is planned which will explore the parallels between the Great Famine and "Third World" issues today.

Additionally, Trócaire is currently in the process of funding three further initiatives:

* An inaugural lecture at Strokestown Park House.

* A series of workshops throughout Ireland aimed at recalling the Great Famine and its parallels with hunger issues today.

* A play by Graffiti Theatre Company, Cork, depicting a family in North America reflecting back on the Great Famine. This play will tour Ireland and will run throughout 1995.

An exhibition is also planned at the Ulster Folk and Transport Museum (see 1.6.9).

1.3 HISTORICAL/CULTURAL/ SCIENTIFIC ORGANISATIONS & PROJECTS

1.3.1 Bandon Historical Society

Cumann Seanchais na Banndan
"Bawnishal"
Hare Hill
Bandon
Co. Cork
Tel. 023-42143
Contact Person: Mr Pat Canniffe

To mark the 150th anniversary of the "Great Famine", Bandon Historical Society is currently engaged in compiling local data about the tragedy, specifically on how the Famine affected the people of their locality.

There are several sites in Bandon which played a significant role in the Famine years. Of particular interest is the Paupers Graveyard in Spring Lane. Hundreds of people from the locality were buried here throughout the Famine. "It was once something of a stigma to be associated with one of these graveyards," says Paddy Connolly, Chairperson of the Historical Society, "but today they are regarded as a significant part of our heritage."

1.3.2 Carrick-on-Shannon and District Historical Society
Summerhill
Carrick-on-Shannon
Co. Leitrim
Telephone: 078-20002 (Daytime) 078-20122 (Evening)
Fax: 078-20788
Contact Person: Mr John Bredin

The Carrick-on-Shannon and District Historical Society has, as one of its primary aims, the establishment in Co. Leitrim of a Famine Workhouse Visitors Centre cum Museum which will provide information regarding life in a Workhouse and the Famine period. Referred to as the "Famine Workhouse Project", it has four identifiable objectives which are:

i) the development of a Visitors Centre/Museum to interpret the Famine.
ii) the restoration and "sensitive" development of the Carrick-on-Shannon Famine Workhouse.
iii) the development of a "Garden of Remembrance" at a Famine Graveyard site, situated adjacent to the Workhouse.
iv) the publication of a historical report detailing the Famine period in Co. Leitrim, with particular reference to the Famine in Carrick-on-Shannon and the Workhouse.

1.3.3 Comhaltas Ceoltóirí Éireann
Cearnóg Belgrave
Baile na Manach
Co. Átha Cliath
Telephone: 01-2800295
Fax: 01-2803759
Contact Person: Mr Labhrás Ó Murchú

Comhaltas is currently carrying articles on the Great Famine in its magazine "Treoir". Special emphasis has been given to the issue of Grosse Ile.

The Comhaltas annual tours of Ireland, Britain and North America will carry a special Famine segment during 1995. The organisation has advised its branches throughout the Irish world to involve themselves in credible local commemorative efforts.

Comhaltas has also advised its study groups in Britain, "Culra", to make the Great Hunger a special theme, followed by visits to various sites in Ireland.

1.3.4 European Association for Potato Research
Pathology Section
Teagasc
Oak Park Research Centre
Carlow
Telephone: 0503-31425
Fax: 0503-42423
Contact Person: Mr Leslie J. Dowley

The European Association for Potato Research will hold a sesquicentennial scientific conference entitled "Phytophthora 150", at Trinity College, Dublin, between September 10-16, 1995.

The conference is being organised to commemorate the 150th anniversary of the first report of late blight in Ireland and the subsequent Great Irish Famine. According to the European Association for Potato Research, this conference provides a unique opportunity to experience the country which has given its name to the Irish Potato and which also suffered more through the hands of Phytophthora infestans.

Topics to be discussed include genetic variation, isozyme analysis, epidemiology, biochemistry, fungicide resistance, chemical and integrated control, meteorology and forecasting, mating types, breeding for resistance and testing for resistance. A bound hardback edition of the proceedings will be available at the meeting.

On Monday, September 11, 1995, the conference will be officially opened by the President of Ireland, Mrs. Mary Robinson.

1.3.5 Federation for Ulster Local Studies
8 Fitzwilliam Street
Belfast BT9 6AW
Telephone/Fax: 0232-235254
Contact Person: Dr Bill Crawford

The Federation for Ulster Local Studies was founded in 1975 as an umbrella group for the whole province of Ulster. The Federation has 80 societies affiliated to it, 40 associate members and 90 individual members.

The Federation "believes that history requires constant reinterpretation to answer new questions and cope with new situations". To facilitate this process, the Federation organised, in association with the Ulster-American Folk Park, Omagh, Co. Tyrone, a seminar on Saturday, 5 November, 1994 entitled "Studying the Great Famine in Ulster". Three academics: Dr. Bill Vaughan, Trinity College, Dublin; Dr. Margaret Crawford, Queen's University, Belfast and Dr. Jim Grant, former lecturer at St. Mary's College, Belfast, presented papers aimed at helping Federation members learn more about the methods and sources of research available on the Great Famine, to assist local studies. At a plenary session following their presentations, Federation members gave an account of projects on the Famine in which they are engaged.

In February 1995, the Federation will organise a seminar at the Public Records Office, Belfast, which will look at documentary evidence available from the Famine period. The Public Records Office in Belfast has, for example, 100 tons of Workhouse Records which are well preserved and processed.

1.3.6 Irish Family History Foundation
2 Kildare Street
Dublin 2
Telephone: 01-6611626
Fax: 01-6621062
Contact Person: Mr John Grenham

The Irish Family History Foundation is planning a series of lectures on the Great Famine and the subsequent exodus of millions of people from Ireland. The Foundation anticipates a growing interest in its work by descendants of Famine immigrants and its 32 branches throughout Ireland are putting in place the necessary infrastructure to facilitate this.

1.3.7 Irish Organic Society
Springmount
Ballyboughal
Co. Dublin
Telephone: 01-8433051
Contact Person: Ms Nicky Kyle

On Saturday, September 23, 1995, the Irish Organic Society will hold an informal symposium at the National Botanic Gardens entitled: "POTATOES, PAST AND PRESENT".

Subjects to be covered will include the importance of genetic diversity in the potato and how this can protect it from diversity in blight; the work of the potato gene bank at the Henry Doubleday Research Association (HDRA); and the history of blight in the Botanic Gardens. Speakers will include Dr. Jeremy Cherfas, Head of the Department of Genetic Resources, HDRA, and Dr. Charles E. Nelson, National Botanic Gardens. There will also be a display of many old and unusual varieties of potatoes.

A potato supper in aid of the work of CONCERN will be held in the evening after the event at the Botanic Gardens.

1.3.8 "Isht Ikhana"
Famine Grave Project
Community College
Dunshaughlin
Co. Meath
Telephone: 01-8259137
Fax: 01-8259548
Contact Person: Ms Geraldine Horgan

"Isht Ikhana" (a Choctaw word meaning 'remembrance'), is the name taken by a group of young people at Dunshaughlin Community College, dedicated to the restoration and marking of a Famine burial site, situated close to the Dunshaughlin workhouse.

"Isht Ikhana" was formed by the young people following their participation in AFrI's 'Famine' Walk from Mullagh, Co. Cavan, to Kells, Co. Meath, in October 1993. Students from the college, who participated in the walk, became interested in the Famine history of their own community. Having visited the burial place associated with the workhouse, the students were appalled by its neglect and committed themselves to its restoration. With the support of their teachers and AFrI, they are currently working with their local Community Council and County Council on this project. The County Council has expressed full agreement with their efforts and has agreed to assist them. A FÁS scheme has been established and it is planned to hold a dedication ceremony in May or June 1995 before the students leave the college.

1.3.9 Kells Enterprise Group
Loyd
Kells
Co Meath
Telephone: 046-41549
Contact Person: Mr Aidan Carry

On the Hill of Loyd, about one mile outside Kells, a mass grave contains the bodies of several thousand poor people, who died in the immediate aftermath of the Great Famine.

Close by, a landlord's "folly", known locally as the "Steeple of Light", was built by many poor people in 1791, at the behest of Lord Headford.

Over the years, a number of local people in Kells have tried to ensure that this site was preserved with the dignity befitting the victims of poverty and hunger who lie here. In recent years, local man, Aidan Carry, together with the Kells Enterprise Group and with the help of FÁS, have begun to develop a theme park around the site.

Since 1991 AFrI has organised an annual October Ulster-Leinster Great 'Famine' walk from Mullagh, Co. Cavan to the Hill of Loyd. Mullagh was the birthplace of St. Killian of Wurzburg (640-689).

In the spirit of St. Killian and the Irish missionary tradition, AFrI seeks to celebrate those Irish people who are working in solidarity with the poor of the "Third World" today. AFrI's 1991 walk was lead by Beirut hostage Brian Keenan (see epilogue) during which he stated: "Famine is a lie". AFrI's 1993 walk was dedicated to the memory of CONCERN volunteer, Valerie Place, who died in Somalia in February of that year.

The Kells Enterprise Group has, in recent years, restored the "Steeple of Light" and has installed a light which is visible from six surrounding counties. The light was switched on by Irish missionary Fr. Niall O'Brien in May 1991 and symbolises Ireland's Golden Age between the sixth and ninth Century, when places like Kells and Mullagh were a "beacon of light" during the Dark Ages. The light also draws attention to the mass grave and reminds us of the scandal of hunger in a world of plenty.

1.3.10 Knockfierna Heritage and Folklore Group
Knockfierna Hill
Ballingarry
Co. Limerick
Telephone/Fax: 069-62713
Contact Person: Mr Pat O'Donovan

Knockfierna Hill, situated in the heart of Co. Limerick commanding a panoramic view of six counties, has been inhabited for over 4,000 years. Associated with the ancient God, Don Fierna, it consists of 200 acres of commonage which in the 1840s became the only hope of survival for the many evicted starving peasants for miles around.

The townland of Knockfierna had a population of approximately 1,000 people before the Great Famine. By 1850, the population had declined to less than 300. Today, there are no inhabitants living in Knockfierna. All that is left are the derelict remains of famine huts, dwellings, potato ridges — a grim reminder of the hardship our ancestors had to bear.

In memory of the people of Knockfierna who either died or emigrated during the Famine period, the Knockfierna Heritage and Folklore Group, under the guidance of Pat O'Donovan and with the help of FÁS, is developing a National Famine Commemoration Park. This will include the restoration of a total of fifteen Famine dwellings on their original sites, around which potato ridges are still visible.

1.3.11 National Botanic Gardens

Glasnevin
Dublin 9
Telephone: 01-8377596
Fax: 01-8360080
Contact Person: Mr Donal Synnott

The Great Famine was caused by the destruction of the potato crop in Ireland in 1845, 1846 and 1847. We know today that the potatoes were destroyed by a minute fungus, called Phytophthora infestans, but , in 1845, that was not known.

The National Botanic Gardens at Glasnevin is Ireland's premier botanical and horticultural institution. In 1995 the Gardens celebrates its bicentenary, having been founded under the direction of the Irish parliament, as a "great national object" to promote botany and agriculture.

On 20 August 1845, the Gardens' curator, Dr David Moore, noticed the first signs of disease on the potatoes growing in Glasnevin, thereby heralding the arrival of Phytophthora infestans in Ireland. Later, David Moore carried out experiments to discover the cause of potato murrain and a treatment for it. By painstaking observation he confirmed that the disease was caused by a fungus, and he almost discovered a method of preventing blight attacking potatoes.

To mark the National Botanic Gardens' place in the botanical history of the Great Famine, a special display of the older varieties of potato will be planted in the vegetable garden, and an information panel will be installed explaining the disease, and the history of the potato in Ireland.

Additionally, in association with CONCERN Worldwide, a special ceremony to mark the beginning of the 150th anniversary of the Great Famine, will be held at the National Botanic Gardens on August 20, 1995.

1.3.12 National Graves Association

c/o Murlough
69 Bayside Walk
Sutton
Dublin 13
Telephone: 01-8321312
Contact Person: Ms Mairéad Kearney

The National Graves Association is a voluntary body which strives to ensure that the dignity of Ireland's historical burial places is preserved. It has already organised a number of visits to some of Ireland's mass Famine graves and is planning its own commemorative activities during 1995. The association would be anxious to ensure that Famine commemorative activities are conducted with dignity and not organised for commercial gain.

1.3.13 St. Cronan's Workshop Association

Grange
Roscrea
Co. Tipperary
Telephone: 0505-21426
Fax: 0505-21753
Contact Person: Mr Paddy Richardson

On September 5, 1994, the St. Cronan's Workshop Association gave the Mid-Western Health Board an undertaking to clean up and develop the old burial ground which is situated on approximately one and a half acres of ground, close to the association's centre. Hundreds of people, in some cases whole families, were buried here during the Famine period. According to Project Co-ordinator, Paddy Richardson, "there is a strong, almost forgotten history there, mainly because the location and overgrowth has created great difficulty in gaining access and has effectively isolated this historic site. All this is going to change!"

The site is currently being cleared and the Workshop Association plans to open it as a memorial garden to the public during 1995. The "Memorial Garden" will be landscaped in a fitting tribute to the history of those interred. It will be maintained by the Centre's Horticulture Unit. The Association hopes that the site, when completed, will become part of the Roscrea Historical Trail.

The success of this project will be due to a partnership approach involving St. Cronan's Workshop Association, the Mid-Western Health Board, Roscrea Theme Town, FÁS, the Office of Public Works and SIPTU.

1.3.14 The "Jeanie Johnston" Project
c/o The Ashe Memorial Hall
Denny Street
Tralee
Co. Kerry
Telephone: 066-27777
Fax: 066-27444
Contact Person: Mr John Griffin

The "Jeanie Johnston" (1847-58), was an emigrant barque which transported Irish emigrants from Blennerville, Co. Kerry, to Canada and the United States during the Great Famine. Plans are currently advancing to build a replica of the Blennerville coffin-ship and sail it to Canada and the United States in 1997/98.

1.3.15 Tidy Towns Association
Famine Cemetery Project
Castlematrix
Rathkeale
Co. Limerick
Telephone: 069-64295
Contact Person: Ms Nora Naughton

The Union Workhouse at Rathkeale was built to house 600 people. By 1847 it was housing twice that number, with an average of 13 dying each week from hunger related diseases. On May 11, 1848, the Guardians of the Rathkeale Union advertised for one and a half acres of land, within a mile of the workhouse to be used as a cemetery. Many inmates of the workhouse were buried there for many years. Cholera swept through County Limerick in 1849 killing an average of 30 people per week in the Rathkeale Workhouse. In May of that year, 81 people died there in one week.

The Cemetery continued to be used through the first half of the 20th Century. The last burial there was in the early 1950s. "Regrettably," says Nora Naughton, secretary of the local Tidy Towns Association, "little more than half of the original cemetery now remains, as the rest was excavated in the early 1960s to become part of a new swimming pool complex, for the enjoyment of the local community."

Currently the Rathkeale Tidy Towns Association has begun the task of restoring the remaining portion of the cemetery. An Ecumenical Service will be held at the restored cemetery in September 1995.

Ironically, the Workhouse which saw so much misery and death for want of food, now, 150 years later, houses a modern beef processing plant!

1.3.16 Workhouses of the West Project
Workers' Educational Association (WEA)
Unit 6
The Buttermarket
Enniskillen
Co. Fermanagh
Telephone: 0365-326914
Fax: 0232-230306
Contact Person: Mr Jack Johnston

One of the core themes within the WEA's Peoples History *plans, over the next two years, will be a project on "The Workhouses of the West". The idea is to mark the 150th anniversary of the Great Famine (1845-47) by publishing a book on a number of West Ulster workhouses. Many of these grim buildings still stand as a reminder of the hardship and suffering of the time. The study will try to examine their role in the various county towns of the West at that time and since then. Indeed, their subsequent history has been equally as important. A number became hospitals, a few factories, while others became schools, a Catholic church and a bakery.*

Classes at Strabane, Limavady, Magherafelt, Lisnaskea, Roslea (for Clones Union), Enniskillen and Irvinestown (Lowtherstown Union), will be joined by groups from Bawnboy (Cavan Union) and Manorhamilton (Leitrim Union), making it also a cross-border study. The six most westerly Ulster counties will all have a contribution to make. It is hoped that each group will contribute a chapter on their respective workhouse. The material will also include the reminiscences of a few individuals who for one reason or another spent part of their lives in these institutions.

The publication and training costs of the project will be borne by the WEA while the two classes in the Republic of Ireland will be financed by the Gulbenkian Foundation. Exchange visits to workhouses North and South will also form part of the project. Jack Johnston of the WEA will be project director and will be the editor of the resulting publication.

1.4   IRISH GOVERNMENT & AGENCIES

1.4.1 Office of the Minister of State
Department of the Taoiseach
Government Buildings
Dublin 2
Telephone: 01-6761107
Contact Person: Minister of State, Avril Doyle, T.D.

At AFrl's seventh annual Great 'Famine' Walk, Louisburgh, Co. Mayo, on May 7 1994, the then Minister for State at the Department of the Taoiseach and the Department of Foreign Affairs, Mr Tom Kitt, T.D., made the following announcement: "....let me assure you that the Government intends to commemorate the Famine in a fitting way. I am pleased to announce that the Taoiseach has asked me to co-ordinate the Government Programme of Commemoration. I will chair an inter-departmental committee which will be based in the Department of the Taoiseach and which will co-ordinate efforts." Minister Kitt went on to say, "As Chairman of this new Government Committee, I welcome as much input as possible from organisations and individuals to ensure that the Famine is commemorated in a fitting manner." Echoing points raised with Mr. Kitt by AFrl on 18 October, 1993, concerning an official Government contribution to Great Famine commemorations, the Minister concluded his address as follows:

"I hope that the commemoration of next year's anniversary will heighten our awareness of the reality that poverty and hunger in our world today are not an issue of charity but of justice. That would be the most fitting memorial for those who lost their lives in this tragic event."

Due to a change of Government in December, 1994, the inter-departmental committee is now chaired by Minister of State, Avril Doyle, T.D. The committee has begun preparation for a Government commemorative programme, further details of which will be available over the next few months. The committee has also expressed the wish to co-ordinate and assist the efforts of other groups.

1.4.2 Department of Agriculture, Food and Forestry
Kildare Street
Dublin 2
Telephone: 01-6789011

Teagasc
19 Sandymount Avenue
Ballsbridge
Dublin 4
Telephone: 01-6688188
Fax: 01-6688023
Contact Persons: Mr John Keating; Ms Amelia Davin

Teagasc, in association with the Department of Agriculture, Food and Forestry, is currently developing a major commemorative exhibition entitled: "The Great Irish Famine — People and Scientific Progress".

The information leaflet on the exhibition, prepared by both bodies, states:

"The Great Famine of the 1840s was a traumatic calamity for the Irish nation, and the single greatest catastrophe of 19th century Europe.

"The destruction of the Famine years gave rise to enormous social, economic and political repercussions. Emigration continued to scatter the people across the globe. The landlord to tenant leasing system was decried with demands for land ownership and self government. The outcome is today's Ireland."

Recalling what life was like in pre-Famine and Famine times, the exhibition will demonstrate achievements on the social front and on the scientific front, in relation to potatoes, since then. It will feature:

- Ireland in pre-Famine days.

- Potatoes — husbandry and cultural practices pre-Famine.

- Blight: spread and consequences — hunger, disease, emigration.

- The post Famine period (1851 – 1900).

- Scientific and social development 1901 - 1950.

- Modern potato husbandry.

- Potato as a food — role in today's diet and lifestyle.

The exhibition will run from 3 — 24 September, 1995, at the Mansion House, Dawson Street, Dublin 2.

1.4.3 Local Authorities

Following the formation of the Government's inter-departmental committee, chaired by Minister Tom Kitt, T.D., one of its first initiatives was to contact local authorities throughout the Republic of Ireland, encouraging them to participate in forthcoming Great Famine commemorative activities. All have responded positively to this request. A list of all local authorities in the Republic is detailed below. Press reports during the latter half of 1994 indicate that many local authorities had already begun the process of debating and planning their initiatives. Specific details of local authority plans can be obtained by writing to the addresses below.

Throughout 1994 the Great Famine Commemoration Committee, based at Tullamore, Co. Offaly (see 1.7.6), contacted local authorities throughout the Republic of Ireland concerning the location of Famine sites in their respective districts. By December 1994, County Councils, marked below with an asterisk, had provided the Commemoration Committee with county maps indicating workhouses, fever hospitals, soup kitchens, food depots, Famine roads and public works, Famine graveyards and potato ridges.

County Councils

Authority	Address	Tel. No.	Manager
Carlow	County Offices, Carlow	0503 -31126	Matt O'Connor
Cavan*	Courthouse, Cavan	049-31799	Brian Johnston
Clare*	Courthouse, Ennis, Clare	065-21616	Tom Dowling
Cork*	County Hall, Carrigrohane Rd, Cork	021-276891	Michael N Dillon
Donegal*	County House, Lifford, Co. Donegal	074-41066	Michael McLoone
Dun Laoghaire/ Rathdown	Town Hall, Dun Laoghaire, Co. Dublin	01-2806961	Kevin O'Sullivan
Fingal	46/49 Upr. O'Connell St, Dublin 1	01-8727777	David Byrne
Galway*	P.O. Box 27, County Buildings, Prospect Hill, Galway	091-63151	Donal O'Donoghue
Kerry*	County Buildings, Tralee, Co. Kerry	066-21111	Dominick P. Darcy
Kildare	St. Mary's, Naas, Co. Kildare	045-97071	Frank Kavanagh
Kilkenny	John's Street, Kilkenny	056-52699	Paddy Donnelly
Laois*	County Hall, Portlaoise, Co. Laois	0502-22044	Niall Bradley
Leitrim*	Courthouse, Carrick-on-Shannon, Co. Leitrim	078-20005	Sean Kielty
Limerick*	P.O. Box 53, County Buildings, O'Connell St, Limerick	061-318477	Michael Deigan
Longford	County Offices, Church St, Longford	043-46231	Michael Killeen
Louth*	County Offices, Crowe Street, Dundalk, Co. Louth	042-35457	John Quinlivan
Mayo	Courthouse, Castlebar, Co. Mayo	094-74444	Desmond P. Mahon
Meath	County Hall, Navan, Co. Meath	046-21581	Roibeard Ó Ceallaigh
Monaghan	County Offices, The Glen, Monaghan	047-82211	Joseph Gavin
Offaly*	Courthouse, Tullamore, Co. Offaly	0506-21419	Sean McCarthy
Roscommon*	Courthouse, Roscommon	0903-26100	Eddie Sheehy
Sligo*	Riverside, Sligo	071-43221	John J. Stewart
South Dublin	P.O. Box 4122, Town Centre, Tallaght, Dublin 24	01-4620000	John Fitzgerald
Tipperary (NR)	Courthouse, Nenagh, Co. Tipperary	067-31771	John McGinley
Tipperary (SR)	Council Hall, Davis Road, Clonmel, Co. Tipperary	052-25399	Seamus Hayes
Waterford*	Arus Brugha, Dungarvan, Waterford	058-42822	Donal Connolly
Westmeath	County Buildings, Mullingar, Co. Westmeath	044-40861	J.A. Taaffe
Wexford*	County Hall, Wexford	053-42211	Seamus Dooley
Wicklow	Council Offices, Wicklow	0404-67324	Blaise Treacy

County Borough Corporations

Cork	City Hall, Cork	021-966222	M. Moloney (Act)
Dublin	Block 1, Civic Offices, Wood Quay, Dublin 8	01-6796111	F. Feely
Galway	City Hall, College Road, Galway	091-68151	P.J. Gavin
Limerick	City Hall, Limerick	061-45266	J. Higgins
Waterford	City Hall, Waterford	051-73501	M.J. Doody

Borough Corporations

Clonmel	Town Hall, Clonmel, Co. Tipperary	052-22100	Ms. B. Kinsella
Drogheda	Courthouse, Drogheda, Co. Louth	041-33511	B.P. Hoey
Kilkenny	City Hall, Kilkenny	056-21076	D.P. O'Brien
Sligo	Town Hall, Sligo	071-42141	J. McNabola
Wexford	Municipal Buildings, Wexford	053-42611	D.F. Curtin

1.5   MEDIA

1.5.1 BBC
Ormeau Avenue
Belfast BT2 8HQ
Telephone: 0232-338879
Contact Person: Mr John Percival/Mr Pete Lawerence

BBC 2 has embarked upon a three-part documentary series on the Irish Famine, to be broadcast in the Autumn of 1995. The series will explore causes, effects and long term consequences of the Famine.

1.5.2 Gael Media
Film and Television Production
Furbo
Co. Galway
Telephone: 091-592533
Fax: 091-592203
Contact Person: Ms Edna McNamara-Connolly

Gael Media is currently planning a three part documentary series entitled "The Untold Story — The Irish in Canada". The series will focus on the impact of the Irish Famine on modern Canadian society. By 1870 for example, mainly due to the Great Hunger, almost one million Irish people came to Canada, representing 25% of the population of British North America. At the last census in Canada of 1986, almost four million Canadians claimed Irish descent.

The themes of the series will be: 1. "Famine and Emigration"; 2. "The Sea: Friend or Foe"; and 3. "Becoming Canadian". The second programme will substantially deal with the controversy of Grosse Ile's interpretation.

1.5.3 Little Bird Company, Film Production
122 Lower Baggot Street
Dublin 2
Telephone: 01-6614245
Contact person: Mr Jonathan Cavendish

Little Bird, the Film Production Company who made "Into the West", is currently working on a four-part drama series entitled "The Hanging Gale", for BBC Northern Ireland and RTE. The drama series, comprising four x 50 minute parts, is located in Donegal and will explore the effects of the Great Famine on a fictitious tenant farmer and his four sons. Little Bird aims to be historically accurate while remaining dramatically viable. The series will be broadcast on BBC Northern Ireland and RTE in 1995.

1.5.4 RTE Radio 1
Donnybrook
Dublin 4
Telephone: 01-2082985
Fax: 01-2083027
Contact Person: Mr Cathal Póirtéir

RTE Radio One have prepared a series of programmes to commemorate the Great Famine. They are as follows:

1. Thomas Davis Lectures — The Great Irish Famine
Sixteen lectures by leading writers from Ireland, Britain, the United States and Australia will reflect on the impact of the Great Famine. Contributors are: Dr Kevin Whelan, Dr Sean Connolly, Dr David Dickson, Dr Margaret Crawford, Dr. Laurence Geary, Dr Peter Gray, Dr Christine Kinealy, Prof Mary Daly, Dr Irene Whelan, Prof James Donnolly, Dr David Fitzpatrick, Dr Tim P. O'Neill, Cathal Póirtéir, Dr. Margaret Kelleher, Prof Cormac Ó Gráda, Patrick Hickey C.C.

The series of lectures will be broadcast on Sunday nights at 8.00 beginning on January 1, 1995 and will be published in book form in January 1995 by Mercier Press as "The Great Irish Famine", edited by Cathal Póirtéir.

2. Gnéithe den Ghorta
A series of lectures in Irish will be broadcast on Raidio na Gaeltachta in March, April and May, 1995, with an accompanying book Gnéithe den Ghorta, curtha in eagar ag Cathal Póirtéir, to be published by Coiscéim in March 1995. Contributors include Prof Joe Lee, Prof Gearoid Ó Tuathaigh, Prof Cormac Ó Gráda, Dr Tomás Ó Néill, Dr Pádraig Ó Laighin, Dr Niall Buttimer, Niall Ó Ciosain, Seán de Fréine, Seamus Ó Cannain, Dr. Kevin Whelan, Sean Ó Tuairisc and Cathal Póirtéir.

3. Famine Echoes
A 16-part documentary series on the English language folklore about the Great Famine to be broadcast weekly from September to December 1995. Gill and Macmillan

will publish the accompanying book Famine Echoes — a folk history of the Great Irish Famine by Cathal Póirtéir in September 1995.

4. Glórtha ón Ghorta

A series of radio documentaries based on the Irish language folklore material about the Great Famine. Coiscéim will publish the accompanying book Glórtha ón Ghorta by Cathal Póirtéir to coincide with the broadcast on RTE Radio 1 and Raidio na Gaeltachta in 1996.

5. Oceans of Consolation

Six 15 minute programmes based on Dr. David Fitzpatrick's book Oceans of Consolation: a personal account of Irish migration to Australia, produced by Cathal Poirteir, will be broadcast during the Summer of 1995

1.5.5 RTE Television
Independent Productions Unit
Donnybrook
Dublin 4
Telephone: 01-2082743
Fax: 01-2082510
Contact Person: Ms Clare Duignan, Commissioning Editor

In the RTE Guide of July, 1994, its Independent Commission Unit advertised its 1995 commission funds for independent productions. Concerning the Famine, the advertisement stated:

"RTE will commission a number of programmes to commemorate the Great Famine, and proposals for either one-off documentaries, or short series, are sought."

RTE's briefing document stated: "Proposals should, in particular, address the impact the Famine has had on the evolution of the Irish national psyche, the relevance of the events of that time for Ireland today, and the cultural and historical significance of the Famine for modern Ireland."

Louis Marcus Productions
12 Fortfield Drive
Dublin 6W
Telephone: 01-4906723

A series of four 30 minute programmes has been commissioned by RTE's Independent Productions Unit to Louis Marcus Productions. This series will, according to Louis Marcus, "endeavour to offer a fresh and surprising view of the Irish Famine, based on recent scholarly review and interpretation that would provide a 150th anniversary commemoration, free of clichés and sentimentality and of real interest to the general audience of today."

The series will, says Marcus, "strive to adopt a multi-layered approach, rather than a baldly chronological one, moving from past to present, along a range of issues that have abiding interest, and facing the uncomfortable questions that the cosily sentimental view of the Famine has so far avoided. It will take the approach of integrating the hard facts and their fresh interpretation with the still live issues to which they give rise. The series will not only be educational but, we hope, of real interest to a wide modern audience."

1.5.6. RTE
Television Programmes
Donnybrook
Dublin 4
Telephone: 01-2083473
Fax: 01-2083095
Contact Person: **Mr David Blake Knox,**
                                              Assistant Director of TV Programmes

RTE Television is currently involved in a co-production with Great North Productions, Canada, and Arthur Lappin Productions, Dublin (see 3.3.1), on a television drama entitled "The Voyage of the Naparima". RTE, together with BBC Northern Ireland, is also involved with Little Bird Company (see 1.5.3) in the production of the four part drama, "The Hanging Gale". A number of other strands of programming will mark the anniversary.

1.6. MUSEUMS AND HERITAGE CENTRES

1.6.1 Cobh Heritage Centre
The Queenstown Story
Cobh
Co. Cork
Telephone: 021-813591
Contact Person: Mr Michael Callopy

Cobh Heritage Centre is currently finalising plans to rework its general emigration theme to incorporate a major Famine focus for the 150th anniversary. It is also developing an association with University College Cork and plans are afoot to institute a course of Famine Studies.

1.6.2 Famine Centre
St. Catherine's
Louisburgh
Co. Mayo
Telephone: 098-66195
Contact Person: Mr John Joe Kilcoyne

Opened in 1991 by Archbishop Desmond Tutu, the Louisburgh Famine Centre was the first in the world dedicated to the memory of Ireland's Great Famine. The idea of the centre was conceived by AFrI, given the extraordinary Famine history of the Louisburgh — Mayo region. The Church of Ireland presented its former St. Catherine's Church for this purpose.

The centre is still in its early stages but it is hoped it will become a focal point for visitors to the area during the forthcoming commemorative years, who will then be encouraged to explore the locality as a place of special Famine interest. Within a ten mile radius of the centre one can find deserted villages and hamlets, Famine walks, hundreds of acres of potato ridges and mass Famine graves. Additionally, given AFrI's involvement in the area since 1988, the concept of linking the Great Irish Famine with hunger issues today is firmly associated with this area.

This is an area and centre with immense potential. AFrI, in association with CONCERN and the Louisburgh Development Company, has enlisted the services of VSI (Voluntary Services International) who has already held a summer work camp in the area aimed at developing a map of the region indicating all the places of special Famine interest. This map will be available for visitors in 1995.

At the handing over of St. Catherine's Church to the Louisburgh Community, on 24 March, 1991, Anglican Minister, the Reverend Jack Heaslip, made the following comments:

"It is curiously suitable that a [Famine exhibit] should be in a former Church of Ireland Church. For many, the Church of Ireland has been associated with the ascendancy and therefore with those who are blamed most for the atrocities of the famine period. Such thinking may be simplistic and over-generalised but is real in the hearts of so many in Ireland and abroad. As an Anglican, I apologise to my Roman Catholic neighbours for the wrongs done to their forefathers by the cruelty of bad landlords. I believe that in the forgiveness of Anglicans by Catholics lies the real beginnings of reconciliation and healing of much of the hurts which can still be felt generations after the famine itself........

"One of the justifications of learning history is the theory that from the past we can learn to avoid making the mistakes of the present. The role of this heritage centre

within a former church building will be most positive if it manages to make the visitor aware of the mirrors of injustice and famine, exploitation and greed. The mirrors are made of the past but the faces reflected are embarrassingly ours. There is much to reflect on."

1.6.3 Famine Museum
Strokestown Park House
Strokestown
Co. Roscommon
Telephone: 078-33013
Contact Person: Mr Luke Dodd

The Famine Museum was opened by President Mary Robinson on Saturday, 14 May 1994. It tells the story of the Strokestown estate during the Great Famine and has a special Development Section with contributions from AFrI, CONCERN, Oxfam and Trócaire.

During the Famine years, the Strokestown estate attracted international attention when the landlord, Major Denis Mahon, was assassinated having attempted to clear two-thirds of his destitute tenants through eviction and assisted-emigration to North America. The museum uses the extensive Strokestown archive to explain the significance of the Famine nationally and to reflect critically on the on-going spectacle of contemporary global poverty and hunger.

This museum will be a major focal point for visitors during the 150th anniversary commemoration, with hundreds of school groups expected to visit during each academic year.

1.6.4 Michael Davitt National Museum
Straide
Foxford
Co. Mayo
Phone: 094-31022
Contact Person: Ms Nancy Smyth

To mark the 150th anniversary of the birth of Michael Davitt (25 March 1846), the Michael Davitt National Museum Committee is planning a series of commemorative events.

The first phase of their plans will be to restore the old Penal Church at Straide where Michael Davitt was baptised. A new updated Michael Davitt exhibition will be housed there.

Having endured the hardships of the Famine years, Davitt's family were evicted from their home in the early 1850s, during the great land clearances in the West of

Ireland. They emigrated to Haslingdon, Lancashire, England. As a boy labourer Davitt lost his right arm in an industrial accident. Educated at a local Wesleyan school, Davitt later became actively committed to the British Labour Movement. In 1879 he returned to his native Mayo, where hunger was stalking the land once more. Davitt realised that if hunger was to be eradicated from Ireland, the political and economic power of the Landlord System would have to be broken. Supported by Charles Stewart Parnell, Davitt founded the National Land League in 1879 which became one of the most important non-violent agrarian movements of the late 19th century, giving birth to the word "boycott".

It is appropriate that Michael Davitt's place in Irish Famine History will be marked in a significant way.

1.6.5 National Museum of Ireland
Kildare Street
Dublin 2
Telephone: 01-6618811
Contact Person: Mr John Teahan

A decision has been taken by the National Museum of Ireland to commemorate the Great Famine. Planning is at an initial stage and museum officials are currently considering how best the museum can reflect the magnitude of the tragedy. An exhibition will be housed at Collin's Barracks which was recently given to the Museum and is currently being converted.

1.6.6 St. Mary's Restoration Committee
National Famine Museum
Kickham Street
Thurles
Co. Tipperary
Telephone: 0504-21133
Contact Person: Mr George Willoughby

The St. Mary's Restoration Committee is currently planning to commemorate the Great Famine with "a dramatic living museum", described as a "giant stage production" of the period. It is intended that the scenes will be remarkably life-like and will transport people back in time to life in Ireland during those years of great hardship.

While plans are currently at the feasibility stage, the museum, when completed, will be housed in the 11th century St. Mary's Church, Thurles. As with St. Catherine's Church, Louisburgh, Co. Mayo, St. Mary's Church has been offered to the local community by the Church of Ireland. Appropriately, the museum will retain a place of public worship within the building.

A 16 x 4 foot model of Thurles in the year 1846 has been made for the museum. The model, which is the result of painstaking work by local historian, Mr. Jim Condon, is based on Trevelyan's Poor Law Valuations at that time.

During recent preparatory renovations of the Church, the committee discovered a complete record of the Thurles and Rahealty Relief Committee, chaired by Archdeacon Henry Cotton and John Gore-Jones, which catalogued the horror of the Famine period. "It is believed that Thurles is one of the very few towns which today has the minutes of its food distribution committee," says Loret Cleary, vice chairperson of the Restoration Committee.

It is hoped that the National Famine Museum will be operational by the end of 1995, to co-incide with the 150th anniversary period.

1.6.7 The Irish Jewish Museum
Walworth Road
South Circular Road
Dublin 8
Telephone: 01-6760737
Contact Person: Mr Raphael Siev

To commemorate the support of a number of Jewish communities world-wide, especially in the United States of America and Britain, The Irish Jewish Museum will be mounting a display recalling their generosity towards famine relief in Ireland during the Great Hunger of 1845-49.

1.6.8 Ulster American Folk Park
2 Mellon Road
Omagh
Co. Tyrone
Telephone: 0662-243292
Fax: 0662-242241
Contact Persons: Mr John Gilmore, Director and Mr John Walsh, Head of Museum Services

The Ulster American Folk Park is planning a full programme of events to commemorate the 150th anniversary of the outbreak of the Great Famine:

- September 7 – 9, 1995: A major international conference on the general theme "Famine and Emigration" will be held at the Park.

- An exhibition on the Famine, jointly with the Public Records Office of Northern Ireland is also planned.

- In the outdoor museum site a single room cabin from the Famine period will

*be re-erected. This will further enhance the Park's function in interpreting
emigration from Ireland in the 19th century.*

- *The Ulster-American Folk Park's major new indoor exhibition "Emigrants: Two
  Centuries of Emigration" also features the Famine — one of the most
  interesting exhibits is a full scale model of a Famine Cabin complete with life
  size models, sound effects, etc.*

- *Since 1989 the Park has been compiling an Emigration Database which
  contains many types of sources — Ships' Passenger Lists, Newspaper
  Notices, Government Reports and Emigrant Letters. A significant number of
  these documents relate to the period of the Great Famine.*

1.6.9 Ulster Folk and Transport Museum
153 Bangor Road
Cultra
Hollywood
Belfast BT18 0EU
Telephone: 0232-428428
Contact Person: Dr Jonathan Bell

*A major exhibition commemorating the Great Famine is currently in hand for
1995. The exhibition will open in March 1995, in association with Trócaire. It will
examine the causes, experiences and remedies of famine; the Irish context and the
modern world. Special reference will be made to Somalia and Ethiopia.*

*Additionally the Ulster Folk and Transport Museum is currently involved with
Trócaire and the Famine Museum, Strokestown, in developing an education pack for use
in schools throughout Ireland.*

1.7   REMEMBRANCE COMMITTEES

1.7.1 An Gort Mór Famine Commemoration Committee
8 North Mall
Cork
Telephone: 021-393572
Fax: 021-393537
Contact Person: Mr Criostoir de Baróid

Formed in March 1994, An Gort Mór Famine Commemoration Committee is a body of "concerned citizens" who are anxious to "vindicate and assert the dignity of our Famine dead". Members of the committee are currently engaged in studying available information, with a view to developing a series of events and participating in other commemorative activities.

1.7.2 Filemore Parents Council
Ballydarrig
Cahirciveen
Co. Kerry
Telephone: 066-72738
Fax: 066-72993 ·
Contact Person: Mr James A. Casey

James A. Casey is a U.S. born engineer currently working in the Cahirciveen area of Co. Kerry. He has a special interest in the Famine era and hopes to encourage regional interest and a local contribution to forthcoming commemorative activities under the auspices of the Filemore Parents Council.

Casey organised an introductory lecture entitled "Americans and the Great Irish Famine — A story of Human Concern" at 8.30 pm on February 4 1995, in the Cahirciveen Heritage Centre. It is hoped that other activities will develop from this lecture.

1.7.3 Galway Great Famine Commemoration Committee
Ballybane
Headford
Co. Galway
Telephone: 091-35359
Fax: 091-755971
Contact Persons: Ms Anna McHugh/Ms Treasa Moore

Formed in 1992, the Galway Great Famine Commemoration Committee is affiliated to the Great Famine Commemoration Committee, Tullamore.

This committee has a slide presentation and commentary entitled "The Great Famine in Connaught, 1845-1847".

1.7.4 Irish National Congress (INC)
Famine Commemoration Ad Hoc Committee
PO Box 2814
Dublin 7
Telephone: 01-8202019
Contact Person: Mr Robert Ballagh

A resolution was passed at the 1994 AGM of the INC to support AFrI's Great 'Famine' Project in whatever way the organisation can. An ad hoc committee of INC members is currently considering its contribution.

1.7.5 Skibbereen Famine Committee
Market Street
Skibbereen
Co. Cork
Telephone: 028-22216
Contact Person: Mr Pat Cleery

Skibbereen has been described as the "epi-centre" of Ireland's Great Famine. With this in mind, the Skibbereen Famine Commemoration Committee has embarked on an ambitious three year project. Phase 1, which is currently in progress, will establish a Famine Trail in and around Skibbereen; will publish a book specific to Skibbereen during the Famine; and will mark the mass grave at Abbeystrewery Cemetery (containing an estimated 8,000-10,000 victims).

1.7.6 The Great Famine Commemoration Committee
Cumann Chuimhneachán an Ghorta Mhóir
"Sheena"
Charleville Road
Tullamore
Co. Offaly
Telephone: 0506-21405
Fax: 0506-21659
Contact Person: Mr Tom Maher

The Great Famine Commemoration Committee was formed in April 1993 and is co-ordinating aspects of the overall 150th commemorative events. Its aims are:

1. To develop national and international awareness of the imminence of the 150th anniversary of the Great Famine in Ireland.

2. Encourage the organising of commemorative events at local, national and international levels.

3. Foster further research and study of the period.

4. To draw up a calendar of commemorative events.

Since its inception, the Great Famine Commemoration Committee has stimulated national and international interest in the Famine anniversary. Additionally, it has engaged in wide ranging correspondence with universities, cultural and historical organisations at home and abroad. In its Press Release of October 4, 1994, the Famine Commemoration Committee announced details of an appropriate presentation being prepared by Hyde Park Barracks Museum, Sydney, as well as interest in commemorating the Famine in South Africa and Poland.

Concerning Famine commemoration activities in the UK, the Press Release stated:

"As a result of contact with universities and third level colleges in the United Kingdom many have expressed interest in making mid-19th century history a focus of study for their students. The institute of Irish Studies at the University of Liverpool plans to mark the 150th anniversary of the Great Famine in Ireland with a comprehensive multi-disciplinary programme. It also hopes to work with other organisations in order to co-ordinate commemorative events taking place in the Liverpool area. Among the other places in Britain which have expressed interest in the commemoration are Derby, Newi College in Wales, Manchester, Brighton, Edinburgh, York, Sunderland, Lancashire, Twickenham, Teeside and Brunel University in London."

1.8 UNIVERSITIES/COLLEGES

1.8.1 Irish Famine Network
Trinity College
Dublin 2
Telephone: 01-6772941 ext 1020
Contact Person: Mr David Fitzpatrick

The Irish Famine Network was founded by Irish Academics and Historians anxious to support and enable local research and systematic analysis of Ireland's Great Famine. With the approach of the sesquicentenary of the Famine, the Irish Famine Network states that "Irish historians are becoming uncomfortably conscious of the absence of a comprehensive study of the Great Famine at local level".

To enable more rigorous and systematic analysis, the network published, in 1993, "Records of the Irish Famine — A Guide to Local Archives, 1840-1855" by Deirdre Lindsay and David Fitzpatrick.

The Irish Famine Network enlists the support of academics from major universities and colleges in Ireland.

1.8.2 St. Patrick's College

West of Ireland Theology Research Association
Maynooth
Co. Kildare
Telephone: 01-6285222
Contact Person: Professor Enda McDonagh

The West of Ireland Theology Research Association is currently exploring the possibility of organising a conference in October, 1995, which will examine ethical issues arising out of the Famine, especially as they apply to contemporary issues of hunger and poverty today. It is planned to hold the conference at the Famine Museum, Strokestown, Co. Roscommon. The conference,entitled: "Famine: A Religious-Ethical Commemoration", is planned to last three days and will include lectures and workshops. Themes to be covered are as follows:

Day 1:   *The Irish Experience*

              1. Religious Interpretations and Ethical Responses.

              2. Still a Famine People. Continuing Religious and Ethical Influences on Protestant-Catholic, North-South and British-Irish Relationships.

Day 2.   *The Contemporary Experience*

              1. The Ethics and Economics of Hunger

              2. Is Land Still Sacred?

              3. Tolerating Genocide? Contemporary Passivity in the Face of Famine and Other Disasters.

Day 3.   *Theological Reflections*

              A. Famine Faith and Providence

              1. A Jewish Perspective

              2. An African Perspective

              3. An Irish Perspective

              B. Eucharist in the Face of Famine

1.8.3 UCC-Tufts International Conference On Development
University College Cork
Room G1
East Wing
UCC
Cork
Telephone: 021-276871 ext. 2010
Fax: 021-275006
Contact Person: Ms Caroline Treacey

The 150th Anniversary of the founding of University College Cork will be celebrated in 1995. As part of the year long anniversary celebration, UCC in association with Tufts University in Boston will host an International conference on Famine, Ageing and Development from November 17th-19th, 1995. "It is," says Caroline Treacey, "pertinent that this conference also marks the 150th anniversary of the Irish Famine".

The conference will examine the significant contribution small economies, including Ireland, have made over the years to alleviate famine and assist developing countries. "Indeed", says Treacey, "Ireland's contribution is noteworthy in that it constantly leads the world in per capita non-government fund-raising for hunger relief". The role small economies can play so as to avoid famine in the decades to come will also be examined during the conference. Subsequent issues concerning ageing will likewise be addressed.

Ireland's President, Mary Robinson, whose concern for the world's poor is recognised internationally, will give the keynote address on November 17th 1995. International leaders of educational institutions, nutritional groups and aid organisations will be present and participate in the conference; as will ambassadors from nations in which Ireland is actively providing relief.

§ 2. BRITAIN

2.1 REMEMBRANCE COMMITTEES

2.1.1 Cumann Chuimhneachán Ghorta Mór na hÉireann
Great Irish Famine Remembrance Association
84 Harrowdene Road
Wembley
Middlesex HAO 2JF
England
Telephone: 081-9023799
Contact Person: Mr Paul Finnegan

The Great Irish Famine Remembrance Association was formed in the Autumn of 1991. It was formed as a response to a concern expressed by members of the Irish community in the Greater London area at the absolute neglect of the Famine period in their formative historical and cultural experience.

Recognising the approaching 150th anniversary as providing the opportunity to rectify this situation, the Remembrance Association is currently developing a series of events. These include:

- Four to five lectures during 1995.

- A joint seminar on the Great Famine on 15 March, 1995, in partnership with the Irish Studies Centre at North London University.

- Lectures, seminars and workshops on the Famine at the Irish Centre, Camden, London, in Spring 1995.

- A joint seminar in Hertfordshire/Bedfordshire with St. Alban's, Hemel Hamstead and Luton Irish societies.

- A workshop on the Great Famine at the annual Leicester Education Conference in Spring 1995.

- An exhibition of contemporary Famine drawings.

- The publication of lectures delivered by various activists and academics.

The Association is also exploring the possibility of erecting a major Great Famine memorial in Liverpool in recognition of the pre-eminence of that city's role in the history of the period.

2.1.2 Great Famine Commemoration Committee (Liverpool)
(Coiste Chuimhneachán an Ghorta Mhóir (Learphoill))
Irish Centre
127 Mount Pleasant
Liverpool L3 5TQ
Telephone: 051-2521679
Contact Person: Mr Neil Doolin

Between the autumn of 1846 and December 1853, about two million Irish people passed through Liverpool, large numbers of them starving because of food *shortage in Ireland. Many dispersed to other parts of Britain, the United States, or elsewhere. Many died in the streets of Liverpool, through starvation, disease or neglect. The city bore the burden of providing for them. The impact on local services was overwhelming.*

The Liverpool Great Hunger Commemoration Committee is an umbrella group comprising the principle Irish community groups in Liverpool. Its objectives are concerned with the appropriate and respectful commemoration of the events in Ireland in the 1840s and the effect they had in Liverpool. These objectives include the provision of lectures, publicity and information concerning the Great Hunger and, in particular, the erection of memorials at appropriate locations as permanent recognition of the events of that period.

2.1.3 Irish World Heritage Centre (Manchester)
10 Queens Road
Cheetham Hill
Manchester M8 8UR
Telephone: 061-2054007
Fax: 061-2059285
Contact Person: Mr Michael Forde

The Irish World Heritage Centre, Manchester, has an ambitious project aimed at building a new £5 million Heritage Centre, which will both reflect on the experience of the Irish Famine emigrants worldwide and celebrate their survival and achievements.

The sod for the new Centre will be turned on September 13, 1995. The building of the Heritage Centre will continue throughout the first three anniversary years of the Great Famine and it is planned to have it operational by 1997.

The Irish World Heritage Centre has a well established interest in the anniversary commemorations. Members of the Centre travelled to Louisburgh, Co. Mayo, for AFrI's third annual Great 'Famine' Walk in 1990, lead by the Choctaw Nation of Oklahoma.

From November 1–3, 1990, the Irish World Heritage Centre invited AFrI and representatives of the Choctaw Nation on a visit to Manchester for a seminar on the Great Hunger. A 'thank you' dinner, in honour of the Choctaw visitors, was also held. During the dinner, Chief Hollis E. Roberts presented an Indian Headdress to the Centre as well as other Choctaw artefacts, which are on continual display

2.2 UNIVERSITIES/COLLEGES

2.2.1 History Department,
Downing College
Cambridge
CB2 IDQ
Telephone: 0223-334800
Contact Person: Dr Peter Grey

2.2.2 History Department
Queens College
Cambridge
CB3 9ET
Telephone: 0223-335511
Contact Person: Dr Brendan Bradshaw

Queens College and Downing College, Cambridge, are jointly planning a conference on the theme of "The Irish Famine and Emigration". Plans are at a preliminary stage and the conference will probably take place in Cambridge in early 1996.

Dr. Peter Grey of Downing College, Cambridge, is currently working on an "Illustrated History of the Irish Famine" to be published in 1995. A U.S. edition will be published by Abrahams, New York. A French edition will be published by Gallimard, Paris.

2.2.3 The Meaning of the Famine
The Irish World Wide
Department of Inter-disciplinary Human Studies
University of Bradford
Bradford BD7 IDP
Yorkshire
England
Telephone: 0274-383986
Fax: 0274-720494
Contact Person: Patrick O'Sullivan

The Irish World Wide *project is, says its editor, Patrick O'Sullivan, "a major academic project, bringing together contributors from all over the world and from every relevant academic discipline, to develop the critical, interdisciplinary, methodologically correct, and genuinely world-wide study of the Irish migrations." Two general volumes, whose underlying theme is the search for work,* Patterns of Migration *and* The Irish in the New Communities, *are followed by more focused volumes,* The Creative Migrant, Irish Women and Irish Migration, *and* Religion and Identity.

Volume 6, the last volume, is called The Meaning of the Famine. *"When I began planning* The Irish World Wide *project I expected to be inundated with offers of material about the relationship between migration and the Famine,"* says O'Sullivan. *"I was worried that the Famine might dominate the project. I decided therefore, to give the Famine its own volume, leaving me free to pick and chose from the expected wealth of famine-related material to create a coherent volume.*

"My strategy turned out to be absolutely correct, but for all the wrong reasons. In my first world-wide trawl I was offered virtually nothing on the Famine. There seemed to be little new research. In a way (and I put this in an extreme form for dramatic effect) it was as if there was a world-wide academic conspiracy to ignore the Irish Famine. We can think of reasons for this. Generally in these islands we are looking for reasons to love one another rather than reasons for hate. The Famine is a controversial subject; and formal academic careers, at least in their initial stages, are not helped by controversy. Some of that controversy has focused around Cecil Woodham-Smith's book, The Great Hunger. *But that book is, in turn, as far as its publishers are concerned, the most successful Irish history book ever...So, we have to put academic neglect alongside a public wish to know."*

"At last," says O'Sullivan, *"thanks to a hard-working team of contributors, we have a Famine volume to be proud of ...* The Meaning of the Famine *shows that, as news of the Irish Famine spread throughout the world, and throughout the pre-Famine migrant Irish communities, the Irish strove to find a way of understanding this experience and of bringing it within an Irish sense of identity. News of the Famine was soon followed by the fleeing Famine victims themselves, bringing with them, written on their own bodies, the evidence of catastrophe."*

"The volume shows," continues O'Sullivan, *"that the task of understanding the great Irish Famine is by no means complete. Chapters on famine historiography and on writing the Famine show that a 'media studies' approach opens up new areas of debate. It concludes with an innovative study of the Irish Famine's world-wide place in famine history and theory."*

The Meaning of the Famine *will be published in 1995, by Leicester University Press, London.*

2.2.4 European Studies Research Institute

University of Salford
Salford M5 4WP
England
Telephone: 061-7455920
Fax: 061-7455556
Contact Person: Dr Frank Neal

The European Studies Research Institute, University of Salford, will host The Great Irish Famine Commemoration Conference on June 3, 1995.

Contributors will include; Christine Kinealy, author of This Great Calamity; *Luke Dodd, Curator of the Famine Museum at Strokestown, who will reflect on "Representing the Great Famine at the end of the Twentieth Century"; David Fitzpatrick, Professor of Irish History at Trinity College, Dublin, who will speak on "Representations of the Irish Famine in Letters to Australia"; Dr. Frank Neal, Senior Lecturer in Economic and Social Statistics, University of Salford, who will present a paper on "Lancashire and The Famine Irish"; and Canon Nicholas Frayling, Rector of Liverpool Parish Church and a member of the Liverpool Irish Famine Commemoration Committee, who will conclude the conference with a reflection entitled "England and the Irish Famine - Some Thoughts".*

§ 3. CANADA

3.1 GROSSE ILE

Grosse Ile was Canada's quarantine island, created to inspect emigration ships entering Canada. In 1847 the medical authorities on Grosse Ile were totally unprepared for the deluge of coffin-ships arriving from Ireland, carrying thousands of suffering and dying passengers. In that year alone, an estimated 15,000 Irish men, women and children were buried in mass graves upon the island. To this day, Grosse Ile is remembered by the people of Quebec as "The Irish Island".

3.1.1 Action Grosse Ile
18 Tigerlily Court
Willowdale
Ontario M2M 4E4
Canada
Telephone: 416-2219789
Fax: 905-8959416
Contact Person: Dr Michael Quigley

Action Grosse Ile is a committee created in June 1992 by Irish community representatives from Metropolitan Toronto, Brampton, Hamilton and Kingston, supported by and working with Irish community groups coast to coast. Their mandate is to ensure that the mass graves of the Irish Famine victims of 1847 are perpetuated as the main theme of the National Historic Park on Grosse Ile and as a permanent monument to the Irish role in the building of Canada.

On August 19–20, 1994, Action Grosse Ile (Toronto) organised a 30 mile pilgrimage from Quebec to Grosse Ile, lead by Don Mullan of CONCERN Worldwide and Wendy Murphy, a Canadian-Irish Nurse who has worked with CONCERN in Sudan and Somalia. The pilgrimage was organised to co-incide with President Mary Robinson's historic visit to Grosse Ile on August 21, 1994.

3.1.2 General Assembly of Irish Organisations
C.P. 624
Mont-Royal (Quebec)
Canada H3P 3GH
Telephone: 514-7447784
Fax: 514-7447952
Contact Person: Mr Padraig O'Laighin.

The General Assembly of Irish Organisations is an umbrella body representing 31 Irish organisations in Quebec.

It was founded in 1992 in preparation for the release of, and to respond to the original "Development Concept" document of Parks Canada.

The General Assembly aims to protect the integrity of Grosse Ile as a major site of Irish historical interest and to ensure it is not damaged by Parks Canada plans to turn the island into a theme park on general Canadian immigration.

The Assembly has been involved in organising a variety of campaigns: to raise public awareness and to change Government policy concerning Grosse Ile; to continually discuss matters with politicians and bureaucrats; to act as a vehicle of public response to the Canadian Government and Parks Canada concerning Grosse Ile and to continually focus on what Grosse Ile essentially is: "L'Ile des Irlandais et Irlandaises, the Irish Island, Oileán na nGael."

3.1.3 Irish Heritage (Quebec)
P.O. Box 8733
St. Foy
Quebec GIV 4N6
Canada
Telephone: 418-6515918
Contact Person: Ms Marianna O'Gallagher

Irish Heritage (Quebec) is an historic, genealogical and cultural society, aimed at preserving the history of the Irish in Quebec. The society's president, Marianna O'Gallagher, is author of "Grosse Ile — Gateway to Canada". Throughout the past decade Marianna has led many visits and pilgrimages to Grosse Ile and will be available to assist groups wishing to visit the island throughout the anniversary years of the Great Hunger.

In 1995, O'Gallagher will publish "Grosse Ile 1847 —Eyewitness" based on letters written by Catholic and Anglican priests working on Grosse Ile at that time.

3.2   HISTORICAL/CULTURAL ORGANISATIONS

3.2.1 Ancient Order of Hibernians
2204 Old Orchard
Montreal
Quebec H4A 3A8
Telephone: 514-4845764
Contact Person: Mr Kevin Muldoon

On the last Sunday of May each year, the AOH organises a mass at St. Gabriel's Church, Point St. Charles, Montreal, followed by a procession to "the Stone" at Bridge Street, close to the Victoria Bridge. A remembrance ceremony is held at the stone for the approximate 6,000 Irish people buried at this site.

The stone was placed there by workmen who unearthed a mass grave while working on the entrance to Victoria Bridge. Most of the people buried in the mass grave were Irish Famine emigrants who, having been cleared at Grosse Ile, travelled from Quebec to Montreal by steamboat. As with the Famine victims buried at Grosse Ile, they too "found in America but a grave".

3.2.2 Irish Canadian Cultural Association of New Brunswick
109 Roy Avenue
Newcastle
New Brunswick EIV 3N8
Telephone: 506-6224007
Contact Person: Mr Farrell McCarthy

The people of New Brunswick are planning a series of commemorative events between 1995—97. Their St. Patrick's week festival at St. John, New Brunswick, will have a special Famine theme during those years. They are also organising tours/pilgrimages to Partridge Island where several hundred Irish people were buried in 1847. Partridge Island was a quarantine station attempting to halt the spread of disease from Irish emigrant ships to St. John, New Brunswick. An Irish Famine exhibition will open at Partridge Island in 1997.

3.3   MEDIA

3.3.1 Great North Productions
11523 100th Avenue
Suite 012
Edmonten
Alberta T5K OJ8
Canada
Telephone: 403-4822022
Fax: 403-4823036
Contact Person: Mr Andy Thomson

Great North Productions, in association with Arthur Lappin Productions, Dublin, and RTE, is finalising a script for a television drama, loosely based around the story "The Voyage of the Naparima" by James Mangan. Whilst this is a fictionalised drama, it nevertheless tells the very real story of a West of Ireland community forced to embark upon a terrifying trans-Atlantic coffin-ship crossing during the Great Famine. The drama will also tell the story of the Grosse Ile Tragedy during the Summer of Sorrows of 1847.

It is hoped to begin production in the Spring of 1995 and to have the drama available for broadcast in the late Fall of 1995.

§ 4. U.S.A.

4.1 ARTS

4.1.1 The Anne Thérèse Dillen Great Hunger Water Colour Exhibition
c/o CONCERN Worldwide
Camden Street
Dublin 2
Telephone: 01-4754162
Fax: 01-4757362
Contact Person: Mr Don Mullan

During 1991 AFrI organised an exposure visit to Ireland for artist Anne Thérèse Dillen, OSU, aimed at deepening her knowledge of the Great Famine and providing her with the opportunity to visit places throughout Ireland of special Famine interest.

Since then, Sr. Dillen has produced a 32 piece water colour exhibition entitled "My Dark Rosaleen" which has been filmed by the BBC, RTE and private film companies. Two of her paintings have recently been reproduced in Helen Litton's "The Irish Famine: An Illustrated History" (Wolfhound Press 1994). The Exhibition is based on some illustrated London News drawings, images of Ireland, contemporary hunger scenes and a creative imagination.

The Exhibition opened at Iona College, New York, on January 31, 1992. Since then, it has spent three seasons at the Famine Centre, Louisburgh, Co Mayo. It is due to return to the United States in the Spring of 1995 where it will begin a nationwide tour in Boston. Sr. Dillen wishes the exhibition to help contribute towards hunger relief in the world today.

4.2 HISTORICAL/CULTURAL ORGANISATIONS

4.2.1 Irish–American Cultural Institute (IACI)
2115 Summit Avenue (5026)
St. Paul
MN 55105
USA
Telephone: 612-9626040
Contact Person: Mr Jim Rogers

The IACI has tentative plans at present to hold a major international symposium in 1995 with the Smithsonian Institute, Washington, D.C. on the Famine and the Famine era.

During 1991 the IACI provided the opportunity for AFrI's Great 'Famine' Project to visit its chapters throughout the United States and Canada, in order to alert its membership and the general Irish-North American community to the importance of the approaching anniversary.

4.2.2 Irish Hunger Commemoration Coalition
c/o The Irish Echo
309 Fifth Avenue
New York NY 10016-6548
USA
Telephone: 212-6861266
Fax: 212-6861756
Contact Person: Ms Claire Grimes

The purpose of the Irish Hunger Commemoration Coalition is to facilitate and co-ordinate the national and international educational and commemorative activities associated with the observance of the 150th Anniversary of the Irish Hunger, 1995-2000. The organisation and effort associated with this coalition are entirely voluntary and co-operative. Its primary goal is to observe the Hunger Commemoration in the most effective manner possible. Two products are anticipated: a DIRECTORY of planned activities and a BIBLIOGRAPHY of information sources.

It is expected that the DIRECTORY will be made available to all participating and contributing organisations. The BIBLIOGRAPHY, expected to be voluminous, will be available upon request to those who will use it for study, research and reference.

4.2.3 The American–Irish Historical Society (California)
3800 Latrobe Street
Los Angeles
CA 90031
USA
Contact Person: Ms Mary Ferguson

On October 3, 1993, the American-Irish Historical Society of California organised a major international symposium entitled "A Commemoration".

They are currently planning follow-up "one speaker" seminars as part of their Famine Commemoration project.

During November 1994 the society co-sponsored, with Irish Network Television, L.A, the screening of "Out of Ireland", a film by Academy Award winning filmmaker, Paul Wagner, and Ellen Casey Wagner. "Out of Ireland" traced the traumatic exodus of eight specific immigrants from 19th century Ireland to the industrialised cities of the United States. The film is substantially based on Professor Kirby Millar's book "Emigrants and Exiles". A companion book to the film has been co-authored by Kirby Millar and Paul Wagner.

A member of the Society, Dr. Arthur Gribben, is currently editing a volume of essays to commemorate the Famine. The volume, to be published by the University of Illinois Press in 1996, will be interdisciplinary and will include fields such as history, folklore, sociology, social economics etc.

4.2.4 The Irish-American Heritage Memorial Committee
145 Wolcott Avenue
Scyracuse
NY 13207
USA
Telephone: 315-4750345
Contact Person: Mr Patrick Ahern

Plans are afoot to develop a $1 million Irish heritage centre which will act as both a cultural centre for Up-State New York and which will tell the story of the Irish. It is envisaged that this centre will be an education centre, reflecting on Irish history and heritage, with special reference to the Great Hunger. A site has already been secured for this project.

The Irish-American Memorial Heritage Committee has a slide show on the Famine which they present to a wide variety of interested groups.

On 19th July 1992, the Irish-American Memorial Heritage Committee organised the first Famine Walk in North America, to coincide with AFrI's 5th annual 'Famine' Walk at Louisburgh, Co. Mayo. Their walk was lead by the Choctaw Nation of Oklahoma. In a letter to the walk organisers, President Mary Robinson stated, "It has been my great privilege to be made an honorary chief of the Choctaw Nation of Oklahoma and I am conscious that the honour bestowed on me will keep alive, in your country and in mine, the memory of their noble deed."

In August 1995, the Irish Heritage Memorial Committee plans to organise a pilgrimage to Grosse Ile. It will symbolically begin at the site of their planned heritage centre.

4.2.5   The Wild Geese
P.O. Box 1088
Greenwich CT 06831
USA
Telephone: 203-5315547
Contact Person: Mr Tom Toohy

The Wild Geese of Connecticut are currently planning a major contribution to Great Hunger Commemorative events. These include:

- *a touring museum/exhibition in the U.S.*
- *an international interdisciplinary conference in the New York area.*
- *a candle commemoration.*

The Wild Geese have sponsored the emigration section of the Strokestown Park Famine Museum and in 1991, sponsored AFrl's Great 'Famine' Walk from Louisburgh to Doolough, Co. Mayo, led by Archbishop Desmond Tutu.

4.3   MEDIA

4.3.1 Celtic Videos
141 East 33rd Street
New York
NY 10016
USA
Telephone: 212-6894853
Contact Person: Mr Larry McEvoy

Celtic videos is currently distributing the Radharc documentary series "When Ireland Starved" throughout the United States and Canada. Since Christmas 1993, over 2000 copies of the series have been purchased across the North American continent.

4.4 NATIONAL MEMORIALS

4.4.1 The Great Hunger Memorial Project (Boston)
JFK P.O. Box 6366
Boston
MA 02114
USA
Contact Person: Mr Francis J. Costello

During a visit to Ireland in May 1987, Francis J. Costello was introduced to AFrI by the late Sean MacBride. MacBride was anxious for Costello to learn of AFrI plans to commemorate the 150th anniversary of the Great Famine. Following his return to the United States, Costello had an article published in Irish-America magazine (July/August, 1987) in which he quoted the founder of the Irish American Cultural Institute, Dr. Eoin McTiernan, as follows: "We Irish Americans are first and foremost the product of our own history and experience, yet very few of us understand or relate to the single greatest event that shaped that heritage. It is as if our Jewish friends had neglected to include the Holocaust in their ethnic memory".

In a letter to Sean MacBride, Costello said he was inspired to write the article after his meeting with AFrI. Costello's article was valuable and important in that it helped to alert the Irish-American community to the importance of the approaching 150th anniversary.

Costello is now the project co-ordinator of Boston's Great Hunger Memorial Project. Designs for the Memorial Project, initiated by former Mayor Raymond Flynn, are based on an 1847 Illustrated London News Sketch of a rag shrouded and starving Irish woman, Bridget O'Donnell and her two hungry children. The monument will incorporate references to the suffering of African people today. It is planned that the monument will be unveiled in the Quincy Market/Docks Square area of Boston, where, during the Great Famine, over 800 coffin ships off loaded hundreds of thousands of Irish immigrants.

In addition to the Docks Square monument the Great Hunger Memorial Project Committee plans to place a marker on Deer Island, Boston's quarantine station, recalling hundreds of Irish people who died and are buried there.

4.4.2 The Great Hunger Memorial (New York)
P.O. Box 290-690
Brooklyn
NY 11229-0013
USA
Telephone: 718-4487198
Contact Person: Mr Bill Whelan

Sponsored by the New York Fire Department Emerald Society, the Great Hunger Memorial Monument will be erected in Battery Park, Lower Manhattan, where the Irish landed during the Famine. The City of New York has granted the property for the monument.

The larger than life monument, depicting a typical Irish family of the Famine era, will be cast in bronze by Irish-American artist, Peter Donohoe. Major fundraising efforts are currently underway to finance the project. It is hoped to have the monument in place by 1995.

4.4.3 The Irish Famine Memorial Inc (Philadelphia)
P.O. Box 390
Sellerville
P.A. 18960-0390
USA
Telephone: 215-7230928
Fax: 215-7230929
Contact Person: Mr James Coyne

The Irish Famine Memorial Inc was started by the Friendly Sons of St. Patrick, Philadelphia. Plans are progressing to unveil a major memorial in the historical area of the city between Penn's Landing and Independence National Park. The area where this memorial will be sited is, according to James Coyne, "considered to be the most historical square mile in the country".

The Friendly Sons of St. Patrick began with a competition to design the memorial, including the landscaping of the area. Six artists (two Irish and four Americans) were shortlisted. The Commission was eventually given to Mr. Ken Thompson, the renowned Irish Sculptor, resident in Midleton, Co. Cork. Ken consulted with AFrI's Great 'Famine' Project concerning background and information prior to his submission

4.4.4 Great Hunger Memorial (San Francisco)
San Francisco Irish Film Festival Inc.
World Trade Centre
Suite 280
San Francisco
California 94111
Telephone/Fax: 415-3921109
Contact Person: Ms Grania Flanagan

A memorial project, dedicated to the victims of The Great Hunger was announced by Grania Flanagan, Director of the San Francisco Irish Film Festival, at the premier of "Out of Ireland", at the Kabuki Theatre in San Francisco, on November 3, 1994.

The San Francisco Irish Film Festival is to request the Parks and Recreation Department of the City to designate a site at Golden Gate Park, on which a suitable memorial will be placed.

The Irish Film Festival has requested the United Irish Societies of San Francisco to dedicate the 1995 St. Patrick's Day Parade to the memory of those who died during the Great Hunger.

Guest of honour at the Irish Film Festival's screening of "Out of Ireland" was Chief Hollis E. Roberts of the Choctaw Nation of Oklahoma. The Mayor of San Francisco, Frank Jordan, presented Chief Roberts with a proclamation from the City and County of San Francisco on behalf of Americans of Irish descent, acknowledging a debt of gratitude. Mayor Jordan said he was proud, as an Irish-American, to personally thank the Chief of the Choctaw people for their humanity towards the Irish people in 1847, when they contributed $170 towards Irish Famine relief. The Mayor also said that he was delighted with the efforts to establish a memorial site and would lend his full support to the efforts.

4.5   POLITICAL/SOCIAL ORGANISATIONS

4.5.1 American-Irish Celtic USA Stamp Committee
954-A Stuyvesant Avenue
Union
New Jersey 07083
USA
Telephone: 908-9642772
Contact Person: Mr Tom Culhane

The American-Irish Celtic USA Stamp Committee has approached the Citizens Stamp Advisory Committee (CSAC) in Washington D.C. concerning a commemorative stamp on the theme of the Great Hunger. The CSAC reports directly to the Post Master General with recommendations for stamp themes. There are, on average, 70 stamp themes issued per year in the U.S. The process takes between three to four years. Over 3,000 people, including senators and members of Congress are supporting this submission.

Mr. Culhane, whose main interest is in coins, has also approached the Citizens Commemorative Coin Advisory Service (CCCAC) concerning a special commemorative coin on the theme of the Great Hunger. In the last 12 years, only 15 themes have been commemorated in coin.

4.5.2 American Ireland Education Foundation, Inc. (AIEF) Political Education Committee (PEC)

Great Hunger Awareness Campaign
54 South Liberty Drive
Stony Point
New York NY 10980
USA
Telephone: 800-777-6807
Fax: 914-947-2599
Contact Person: Mr Frank Morris (Telephone: 717-737-7013)

Founded in 1975, the AIEF-PEC describes itself as "a national network of Americans who work through the democratic process to bring about the peaceful reunification and independence of Ireland". A non-profit organisation, it disseminates news to its members, the general public and the electronic and print media. Through communicating and educating, the AIEF-PEC hopes to advance the prospects of peace in Ireland. Members are encouraged to write or call elected officials or members of the press in advocating a recommended course of action.

As part of its communicate/educate efforts, the AIEF-PEC has initiated a fact gathering/fact referencing programme on the "Great Hunger — 1845 – 1849". Information has been gathered on events commemorating the 150th anniversary of this watershed event in Irish and American history. Contacts can be supplied for events in Ireland, the US, Canada and, hopefully, in Australia, New Zealand and Argentina.

Those wishing to supply information on any planned 150th anniversary activity, or to request information on events in the US or abroad, can do so by contacting the American Ireland Education Foundation, as listed above.

4.5.3 Famine Commemoration Committee

Ancient Order of Hibernians in America
351A Boston Post Road
East Lyme
CT 06333
USA
Telephone: 203-7398216
Contact Person: Mr James J. Gallagher

The AOH Famine Commemoration Committee and the national "Irish Hunger Commemoration Coalition" are undertaking efforts to facilitate and co-ordinate a strong educational component to any and all commemorative activities in North America, Ireland, the U.K. and Australia. The AOH has committed $5,000 towards the erection of *a memorial marker on a mass grave in Ireland; is working with the National Library to co-ordinate an American tour of the Library's Famine exhibit in 1996; a pilgrimage to Grosse Ile, Quebec, Canada is planned (most likely for 1997), and the AOH is also working to have "A Day of Remembrance" observed in 1996 with a minute silence contained therein.*

The AOH is also in contact with the Irish Government, exploring the possibility of a joint Ireland/US commemorative stamp.

4.6   UNIVERSITIES/COLLEGES

4.6.1 Anthropology Program
Illinois State University
Campus Box 4640
Normal, Il 61790-4640
USA
Telephone: 309-4383827
Fax: 309-4387177
Contact Person: Dr Charles E. Orser

With the assistance of seven students, Charles E. Orser, Professor of Anthropology, Illinois State University, began an archaeological study of Gorttoose, a townland once on the estate of the Strokestown Park House, County Roscommon during June and July 1994. The research is being conducted in association with the Famine Museum at Strokestown Park House and with the in-kind assistance of University College, Galway, and Trinity College, Dublin. The landlord at Strokestown, Major Denis Mahon, evicted the men and women of Gorttoose in 1847 at the height of the Great Famine. For his efforts, Major Mahon was eventually assassinated.

The rationale for the research stems from Dr. Orser's long association with the archaeology of New World African slavery. Dr. Orser has written three books and over 35 professional articles on historical archaeology.

The belief that Irish peasants had nothing and so are not amenable to archaeological study mirrors a similar belief once held about slaves. "Over the past several years," says Orser, "archaeologists have made many startling discoveries about slaves. Their research is changing the way we think about slave personal possessions, quality of life, dietary habits, and religious observations."

During the research in June and July, 1994, the student team found three sites suitable for future excavation. One site contains standing buildings probably inhabited during the famine, and another contained hundreds of artefacts scattered across the ground surface. Using soil phosphate testing at a third site, the students found a non-

destructive method of testing the ground for the presence of past settlements. The students also conducted archival research in Strokestown and Dublin as part of the project.

"The silent peasants of Gorttoose have much to tell us," says Orser. With proper funding, he hopes to continue this anthropological research in Strokestown for many years, eventually expanding it to Counties Galway and Mayo.

4.6.2 The Ireland House Conference on Hunger
New York University
1 Washington Mews
New York NY 10003
USA
Telephone: 212-9983950
Fax: 212-9954373
Contact Person: Dr Bob Scally/Ms Eliza O'Grady

The Ireland House Conference on Hunger will meet on May 19 and 20, 1995, commemorating the 150th anniversary of the Famine in Ireland. Although the Irish Famine is the occasion for the meeting and the focus of the first day's sessions, its overall aim is to assemble leading thinkers on the question of hunger worldwide, both historically and in the present, to help clarify an agenda for future research.

An equal priority is to offer the public in New York ready access to informed thinking on the subject, aided by an extensive use of media and the arts. All lectures, discussions and accompanying performances, films and exhibits are open to the public.

The conference will focus on three integrated topics, beginning with "Hunger in Ireland", followed by "Hunger and History: Comparative Perspectives" and ending with "World Hunger and Political Economy". The keynote speech will be given on Friday evening, May 19, 1995, by President Mary Robinson.

§ 5. AUSTRALIA/NEW ZEALAND

5.1 Hyde Park Barracks
Queens Square
Macquarie Street
Sydney NSW 2000
Telephone: 02-2238922
Fax: 02-2233368
Contact Person: Mr Lynn Collins

As the first staging point for orphan children and young women from Famine racked Ireland seeking new prospects in the colony of New South Wales, Hyde Park Barracks aims to present a series of activities documenting the journeys of those pioneers.

An exhibition "A Body of Troublesome Girls", tracing female immigration through the Barracks (1848-1886), will be supplemented by a series of lectures conducted around the docks, harbour, Quarantine Station and Cathedral, dealing with boatloads of young immigrants and their progress in the colony.

The Hyde Park Barracks Museum aims to establish contacts with descendants of the first wave of Irish immigrants, to establish joint ventures with rural communities founded by early Irish settlers in Australia and make links with points of departure in Ireland.

5.2 Irish Studies Centre
P.O. Box 178
University of Queensland
St. Lucia QLD 4067
Telephone: 07-3651111
Fax: 07-3651199
**Contact Person: Ms Catherine Manathunga (President);
Dr Jennifer Harrison**

The Irish Studies Centre based in Brisbane is holding a weekend seminar on the Great Famine on 22-23 April 1995 at the University of Queensland. This initial commemorative activity will be divided into sessions which will address topics such as looking at representations of the Famine in contemporary literature and other cultural expressions; linking with Australian experiences such as drought; as well as providing a background to the Famine in Ireland and its effects both at home and in the Australian context.

The format is designed around panels with a chairperson to encourage lively audience interaction, stimulating wide debate.

5.3 Letter from Embassy of Ireland, Australia

Ambasáid na hÉireann
Embassy of Ireland
20 Arkana Street
Yarraluma ACT 2600
Australia
Telephone: (06) 273 3022
Facsimile: (06) 273 3741

FACSIMILE MESSAGE

TO: Don Mullan, CONCERN, Dublin
FROM: Declan Smyth, Second Secretary, Embassy of Ireland
DATE: 14 September 1994
PAGES: One (1)
I refer to our telephone conversation on 12 September concerning commemoration of the 150th anniversary of the Famine next year. The Embassy is aware that a number of Irish societies, both here and in New Zealand, do intend to mark the anniversary. Planning, however, is at a very early stage. In these circumstances you may wish to revert to us early in the new year.

END.

§ 6. SOUTH AFRICA

The following information has been kindly supplied by the Great Famine Commemoration Committee, Tullamore, Co. Offaly.

6.1   The History Department
       University of Durban-Westville
       P/Bag Z54001
       Durban 4000
       Telephone: 031-8202145
       Fax: 031-8202383
       Contact Person: Professor Donal P. McCracken (Acting Dean of Arts)

The Ireland and South Africa Project hopes to have some lectures on the Great Famine in Ireland in November 1995, at the University of Durban-Westville.

PUBLICATIONS AVAILABLE

Author: Bourke, A. and Lamb, H.
Title: "The Spread of Potato Blight in Europe in 1845—6 and the Accompanying Wind and Weather Patterns"
Publisher: Meteorological Service, Dublin, 1993
ISBN: 0952123207

ℰℴ

Author: Byrne, Louie
Title: "Cry The Cursed Land (Ireland's Holocaust)"
Publisher: Premier Books, Luton, 1994
ISBN: 095242780X

ℰℴ

Author: Bourke, Austin
Title: "Visitation of God — the Potato and the Great Irish Famine"
Publisher: The Lilliput Press, 1992
ISBN: 0946640939

ℰℴ

Author: Campbell, Stephen J.
Title: "The Great Irish Famine"
Publisher: Famine Museum, Strokestown, 1994
ISBN: 095235411X

ℰℴ

Author: Conlon-McKenna, Marita
Title: "Under the Hawthorn Tree" (Children's Fiction)
Publisher: The O'Brien Press, 1991
ISBN: 0862782066

ℰℴ

Author: Coogan, Beatrice
Title: "The Big Wind"
Publisher: Annalivia Press, 1969
ISBN: 1871311276

֍

Editor: Crawford, E.M.
Title: "Famine: The Irish Experience 900 – 1900"
Publisher: Edinburgh, 1989

֍

Author: Curtis, Liz
Title: "The Cause of Ireland — From The United Irishmen to Partition"
Publisher: Beyond the Pale Publications, Belfast, 1994
ISBN: 0951422960

֍

Author: Daly, Mary
Title: "The Famine in Ireland"
Publisher: Dúndealgan Press, 1986
ISBN: 0852211082

֍

Editors: Edwards, R. and Williams, T.
Title: "The Great Famine — Studies in Irish History"
Publisher: The Lilliput Press, 1994
ISBN: 094664094X

֍

Author: Fitzpatrick, David
Title: "Oceans of Consolation: A Personal Account of Irish Migration to Australia"
Publisher: Cork University Press, 1995
ISBN: 1859180353 (Hardback) 1859180361 (Paperback)

֍

Author: Gallagher, Thomas
Title: "Paddy's Lament"
Publisher: Poolbeg Press, 1986
ISBN: 1853710105

Author: Kinealy, Christine
Title: "This Great Calamity, The Irish Famine 1845-52"
Publisher: Gill and Macmillan, 1994
ISBN: 0717118819 (Paperback) 0717118320 (Hardback)

℘

Editors: Lindsay, D. and Fitzpatrick, David
Title: "Records of the Irish Famine — A Guide to Local Archives, 1840-1855"
Publisher: Irish Famine Network, Dublin, 1993
ISBN: 0952258803

℘

Author: Litton, Helen
Title: "The Irish Famine: An Illustrated History"
Publisher: Wolfhound Press, 1994
ISBN: 0863274277

℘

Editors: Lucking R. & O'Sullivan P.
Title: "The Meaning of the Famine", Vol. 6, The Irish World Wide
Publisher: Leicester University Press
ISBN: 0718514262

℘

Author: Lyons, S.S.
Title: "Ireland Since the Famine"
Publisher: Spontana Press, 1963
ISBN: 0006860052

℘

Author: MacKay, Donald
Title: "Flight From Famine — The Coming of the Irish to Canada"
Publisher: McClelland and Stewart Inc., Toronto, 1990
ISBN: 0771054432

Author: McBride, Doreen
Title: "When Hunger Stalked the North"
Publisher: Adare Press, Banbridge, 1994
ISBN: 1899496017

ℰℴ

Author: Macken, Walter
Title: "The Silent People" (Fiction)
Publisher: Pan, 1965
ISBN: 0330303287

ℰℴ

Author: Mangan, James J.
Title: "Famine Diary" (Historical Fiction)
Publisher: Wolfhound Press, 1991
ISBN: 0863273009

ℰℴ

Author: Miller, Kerby A.
Title: "Emigrants and Exiles — Ireland and the Irish Exodus to North America"
Publisher: Oxford University Press, 1985
ISBN: 0195051874

ℰℴ

Authors: Miller, Kerby and Wagner, Paul
Title: "Out of Ireland — The story of Irish Emigration to America"
Publisher: Aurum Press Ltd, 1994
ISBN: 1854103075

ℰℴ

Author: Mokyr, Joel
Title: "Why Ireland Starved: A Quantitative and Analytical History of the Irish
            Economy, 1800   1850"
Publisher: Allen and Unwin, 1985

Editor: Morash, Christopher
Title: "Hungry Voice" (Poetry)
Publisher: Irish Academic Press, 1989
ISBN: 0716524538

℘

Author: Mullen, Michael
Title: "The Hungry Land" (Fiction)
Publisher: Poolbeg Press Ltd, 1993
ISBN: 185371240X

℘

Author: O'Connor, John
Title: "The Workhouses of Ireland"
Publisher: Anvil Books, 1994
ISBN: 0947962719

℘

Author: O'Flaherty, Liam
Title: "Famine" (Fiction)
Publisher: Wolfhound Press, 1984
ISBN: 0863270433

℘

Author: Ó Gráda, Cormac
Title: "Great Irish Famine"
Publisher: Pan MacMillan, 1992
ISBN: 0333398831

℘

Author: Ó Gráda, Cormac
Title: "Ireland — A New Economic History, 1780 — 1939"
Publisher: Oxford University Press, 1994
ISBN: 0198202105

Author: Ó Gráda, Cormac
Title: "An Drochshaol: Bealoideas agus Amhráin"
Publisher: Coiscéim, Dublin, 1994

℘

Author: O'Rourke, Canon John
Title: "The Great Irish Famine"
Publisher: Veritas Publications, 1989
ISBN: 185390130X (Paperback)   1853900494 (Hardback)

℘

Author: O'Tuathaigh, Gearóid
Title: "Ireland before the Famine"
Publisher: Gill and Macmillan, 1993
ISBN: 0717117839

℘

Editor: Póirtéir, Cathal
Title: "The Great Irish Famine"
Publisher: Mercier Press, 1995
ISBN: 1856351114

℘

Editor: Póirtéir, Cathal
Title: "Gnéithe den Ghorta"
Publisher: Coiscéim, Dublin, 1995

℘

Author: Póirtéir, Cathal
Title: "Famine Echoes — a Folk History of the Great Irish Famine"
Publisher: Gill and Macmillan, September 1995
ISBN: 0717123146

Author: Póirtéir, Cathal
Title: "Glórtha on Ghorta"
Publisher: Coiscéim, Dublin, 1996

℘

Author: Quinn, Peter
Title: "The Banished Children of Eve" (Historical Fiction)
Publisher: H. Hamilton, 1994
ISBN: 0241002435

℘

Author: Rees, Jim
Title: "A Farewell to Famine"
Publisher: Arklow Enterprise Centre, 1994
ISBN: 0952202905 (Case Bound) 0952202956 (Paper Bound)

℘

Author: Salamam, Redcliff
Title: "The History and Social Influence of the Potato"
Publisher: Cambridge Paperback Library, 1970
ISBN: 521316235

℘

Author: Scally, Robert
Title: "The End of Hidden Ireland — Rebellion, Eviction and Emigration"
Publisher: Oxford University Press, 1995
ISBN: 0195055829 (Hardback)

℘

Author: Smyth, Alfred
Title: "Faith, Famine and Fatherland"
Publisher: Four Courts Press, 1993
ISBN: 1851821090

℘

Author: Somerville, Alexander
Title: "Letters from Ireland during the Famine — 1847"
Editor: Snell
Publisher: Irish Academic Press, 1994
ISBN: 0716525305 (Hardback)   0716525453 (Paperback)

℘

Author: Vaughan, William E.
Title: "Landlords and Tenants in mid-Victorian Ireland"
Publisher: Oxford University Press, 1994
ISBN: 019820356X

℘

Editor: Vaughan, William E.
Title: "New History of Ireland" (Vol. 5)
Publisher: Oxford University Press, 1989

℘

Author: Woodham-Smith, Cecil
Title: "The Great Hunger"
Publisher: Penguin, 1962
ISBN: 014014014515X

℘

Author: Whyte, Robert
Title: "1847 Famine Ship Diary"
Editor: James J. Mangan
Publisher: Mercier Press, 1994
ISBN: 1856350916

℘

Title: "British Parliamentary Papers, 1800-1900" (8 volumes)
Publisher: Irish Academic Press

Epilogue:

Famine is a Lie

by

Brian Keenan

Brian Keenan was born in Belfast in 1950. In 1985, while teaching at Beirut University, he was taken hostage. His book, "An Evil Cradling", tells the story of four and a half years of horrific detention. He was released on August 24, 1990.

Before an assembly of almost 1,000 people in Mullagh, Co. Cavan, on Saturday 11 October 1991, Brian Keenan spoke of the Great Irish Famine of 1847 and world hunger today. The occasion was AFrI's annual walk of remembrance to highlight present day hunger worldwide. Brian Keenan led the assembled people from Mullagh, birthplace of Saint Killian, to the Hill of Loyd in Kells, where a mass grave contains the bodies of several thousand poor people.

In his speech, Mr. Keenan stated that 1847 was a date stamped on the minds and imagination of more people than meagre mathematics could compute. After almost a century and a half, people are still compelled by this moment in history.

———————————◆———————————

"1847 — the roads are littered with the fleshy skeletons of our Irish dead. And where the living live, if life it could be called, it was a kind of quarter existence. People were feebly and incredibly struggling. Struggling against a plethora of disease and contagion, rife and devastating, and about which one can only remark — that life existed in such an unholy cauldron speaks loudly of the very miracle that life must surely be.

"1847 —cast your mind's eye back. For each of us have the power to see and know our history if we choose. Ireland is a wasteland, a desolation so profound that even the mind's eye flinches at the sight. It seems the land itself, the very earth is groaning with the kind of absolute despair that makes the spirit cry out for the sanctuary of death.

"Let us tone down our picture with reason, with the language of cause and effect. The historian has sought a way to serve us up our history in more palatable dimensions. I would not seek to add or detract from the historical reasons. Suffice it to say that 1847 was not simply a natural disaster. To call it such is an insult to our intelligence and an even greater one for the tens of thousands who departed this life in the most abominable agony. The historical record is very clear and readily available for those who care to read it. The disease in the potato harvest was only one kind of disease. There was another, more rank and insidious. A whole social, economic and political system that survived on arrogance, oppression, indifference — a system that believed in the vastness of its conceit that some were more equal than others — a cultural superiority that spoke of a divine right of life — a self selecting elitism — a political and economic system shored up by bones and broken bodies of humanity.

"I speak now of how it is, only when we reach out beyond ourselves to embrace, to understand, and to finally overcome the suffering of another that we become whole in ourselves. We are enlarged and enriched as another suffering reveals us to ourselves, and we reach out to touch and embrace it.

"More importantly I am convinced and cannot be unconvinced, that in this day and age, with our technology and great humanism, and our beef and butter mountains, our wine lakes, our rat infested grain stores, that famine on the face of the earth is a lie. For we have the means, the skills and the ability to eradicate it as we have done during the pestilence of the Middle Ages. One thing stands wanting, and glaringly so — have we the will, or, are we in the lines of W.B. Yeats, "Fat-Fingered and fumbling in a greasy till, adding the half-pence to the pence, and prayer to shivering prayer?"

"Does our concern for our own society and happiness make us co-conspirators against humanity?

───────────◆───────────

"One thought I bring you. History is not random. All is given and all is purposeful. Our past is not over and done with. We have the facility of memory and imagination. It is not so much what we can learn from this confrontation with our past. More importantly, what can we do with that knowledge? Because we have known and can know suffering — we know that famine, hunger and all that is the cause of it is perverse, obscene and an abomination before our humanity. If we are constantly compelled to rehumanise and deepen our humanity, then we must of consequence seek ways and means to eradicate this abomination. If we commit ourselves to life, we must commit ourselves to the destruction of everything that is anti-life, even, and especially, if it wears the guise of politics, of global economics or some vision of cultural superiority. We must increasingly seek a way to overcome it. For where there is human suffering, there is, most certainly, a vast and concealed cancer of injustice."

───────────◆───────────

———◆———

CONCERN Worldwide is a voluntary non-governmental organisation devoted to the relief, assistance and advancement of peoples in need in less developed areas of the world.

CONCERN Worldwide has offices at the following addresses:

Camden Street, Dublin 2
Telephone: 01-4754162 Fax: 01-4757362

47 Frederick Street, Belfast BT1 2LW
Telephone: 0232-231056 Fax: 0232-330839

Level 2, 80 Buchanan Street, Glasgow G1 3HA
Telephone: 041-2213610 Fax: 041-2213708

248/250 Lavender Hill, Clapham Junction, London, SW11 1LG
Telephone: 071-7381033 Fax: 071-7381032

104 East 40th Street, Room 903, New York NY 10016, USA
Telephone: 516-5578000 Fax: 516-5578004

———◆———

Printed on recycled paper